MATH TRAILBLAZERS™

Grade 5

Unit Resource Guide
Unit 14
Using Circles

SECOND EDITION

A Mathematical Journey Using Science and Language Arts

KF

KENDALL/HUNT PUBLISHING COMPANY
4050 Westmark Drive   Dubuque, Iowa 52002

A TIMS® Curriculum
University of Illinois at Chicago

UIC The University of Illinois at Chicago

The original edition was based on work supported by the National Science Foundation under grant No. MDR 9050226 and the University of Illinois at Chicago. Any opinions, findings, and conclusions or recommendations expressed in this publication are those of the author(s) and do not necessarily reflect the views of the granting agencies.

3 4 5 6 7 8 9 10   07 06 05 04

LETTER HOME

Using Circles

Date: _____

Dear Family Member:

In this unit, your child will use a compass and straightedge to draw lines, angles, circles, and other shapes. In particular, this unit focuses on investigating circles through a variety of hands-on activities.

Students will discover a special number in mathematics—π (pronounced pie). π arises out of the natural world. It is found by dividing the circumference of a circle (the distance around the outside) by its diameter (the distance across the circle through the center). For any size circle, the result of this division is always π—a little more than 3. Thus the distance required to go around a circle is a little more than three times the distance required to go across the circle through the middle. Students will discover this relationship in a laboratory investigation where they measure, graph, and analyze the circumference and diameter of different-sized round cans or lids.

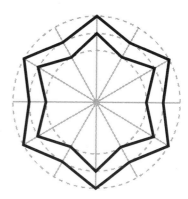

An Arabic design made with a compass and a straightedge

As we explore circles in school, consider doing the following:

- **Look for Designs.** Many designs in tiles and wall coverings include circles. Talk together about the geometry of the designs. Ask your child to show you the circumference, diameter, radius, chords, or center of these circles.

- **"About 3."** Ask your child to demonstrate the relationship between the circumference and diameter of a circle. Provide a can or lid and some string to help in the demonstration.

Thank you for your continued support.

Sincerely,

_____

We will need cans and plastic, circular lids of various sizes to complete the laboratory investigation in class. Please send any unneeded cans or lids to school with your child.

UNIT OUTLINE

Using Circles

Pacing Suggestions

This unit is designed to be completed in 12 to 14 days as shown on the Unit Outline below.

- Lesson 5 *Circle Graphs* makes connections between mathematics and science. Students can use science time for reading circle graphs on endangered species.
- Lesson 6 *Practice and Problems* includes a series of word problems about circles. The problems can serve as homework or assessment. They are also appropriate to use in class with a substitute teacher since preparation is minimal.

Components Key: SG = Student Guide, DAB = Discovery Assignment Book, AB = Adventure Book, URG = Unit Resource Guide, and DPP = Daily Practice and Problems

	Sessions	Description	Supplies
LESSON 1 **Exploring Circumference and Diameter** SG pages 426–427 DAB page 213 URG pages 22–29 DPP A–B	1	**ACTIVITY:** Students explore the circumference and diameter of circles. They estimate that the circumference is about three times the length of the diameter.	• glue • string • scissors • cans and lids of various sizes
LESSON 2 **Circumference vs. Diameter** SG pages 428–434 URG pages 30–43 DPP C–H	3–4	**LAB:** Students measure the circumference and diameter of circles. They plot their measurements in a graph and find that the circumference of any circle is π times the length of the diameter. **ASSESSMENT PAGE:** *Going Around in Circles*, Unit Resource Guide, page 41.	• cans and lids of various sizes • rulers • string or adding machine tape • calculators

	Sessions	Description	Supplies
LESSON 3 **Constructing Circles with Terry** SG pages 435–439 DAB page 215 URG pages 44–57 DPP I–N	3	**ACTIVITY:** Students learn about circles and use rulers and compasses to draw, measure, and label them.	• rulers • compasses • protractors • blank paper
LESSON 4 **Complex Constructions** SG pages 440–444 URG pages 58–73 DPP O–T	3	**ACTIVITY:** Students use a compass and a ruler to copy and construct shapes. **ASSESSMENT PAGES:** *Circles and Constructions,* Unit Resource Guide, pages 69–70.	• protractors • rulers • compasses • blank paper
LESSON 5 **Circle Graphs** SG pages 445–449 DAB pages 217–219 URG pages 74–84 DPP U–X	2	**ACTIVITY:** Students interpret data using circle graphs. They use fractions, decimals, and percents to represent data. They make circle graphs using small centiwheels.	• calculators • scissors • rulers • small centiwheels • compasses
LESSON 6 **Practice and Problems** SG pages 450–451 URG pages 85–87	**– OPTIONAL LESSON –**		
	1	**OPTIONAL ACTIVITY:** Students solve a variety of problems using concepts learned in this and previous units.	• calculators

A current list of connections is available at www.mathtrailblazers.com.

Literature

Suggested Titles

- Lasky, Kathryn. *The Librarian Who Measured the Earth.* Little, Brown, and Company, New York, 1994.
- Levy, Judith (ed.). *The World Almanac for Kids, 1998.* Funk and Wagnalls, Mahwah, NJ, 1997.

Software

- *Fraction Attraction* develops understanding of fractions using pie charts and other materials.
- *The Geometer's Sketchpad* gives students the opportunity to create their own geometric drawings.
- *Graph Master* allows students to enter data and make graphs.
- *Logo* helps students develop spatial reasoning and an understanding of geometry.

PREPARING FOR UPCOMING LESSONS

In Lessons 1 and 2, students measure the circumference and diameter of cans and lids. Ask students to bring in cans and lids of various sizes. A good selection of circular objects for students to measure includes: empty spools of thread or film canisters for small objects, soup cans or masking tape rolls for medium objects, and coffee cans or large lids for large objects.

BACKGROUND

Using Circles

Much of the current thinking on how children learn geometry has been influenced by the research of two Dutch educators, Dina van Hiele-Geldof and Pierre van Hiele. Based on their observations, the van Hieles theorized that there are five levels in the development of geometrical thinking. Each of these levels was described in the Background of Unit 6. The work in this unit focuses on Level 1 and Level 2. Since the van Hieles labeled their levels beginning with Level 0, these are actually the second and third stages of development.

Level 1 activities in this unit involve students in exploring and identifying the circumference, radii, diameters, center, and chords of a circle. Students learn to use a compass and a ruler to copy and construct shapes. The activities at Level 1 introduce much new vocabulary. We have found that if the teacher introduces mathematical vocabulary within a context and uses it along with everyday vocabulary, students will see the need for the terminology and begin to use it. While precise language is necessary to progress in mathematics, it is also necessary to use everyday language for students to internalize concepts (Clements and Battista, 1992). For example, in mathematics the term **circle** refers to the curve that is equidistant from the center. In everyday language, a circle can mean the circular region.

Activities in this unit facilitate student thinking to move toward van Hiele Level 2. In Level 2, students explore relationships. Students informally explore the relationship between the circumference and the diameter of a circle in the first activity. Using string to estimate the relationship between the lengths of the diameter and circumference of a circle, students find that it takes approximately three diameters to

"wrap around" the circumference. In the next activity, they then complete a laboratory investigation where they find a more accurate estimate for the ratio $\frac{C}{D}$, i.e., the ratio of circumference to diameter. This ratio, which is the same for each circle, is called π or **pi.** This is the Greek letter corresponding to p and is pronounced "pie." Working with concrete materials enables children to gain insights into this relationship (Fuys, et al., 1988).

Approximating π

One of the earliest accurate estimates of π is credited to Archimedes circa 240 BCE. Archimedes inscribed and circumscribed polygons about a circle. See Figure 1. Since it is easy to find the perimeter of a polygon, as opposed to finding the circumference of a circle, Archimedes was able to create a range for the value of π. As he drew polygons with more and more sides in and about the circle, he was able to get better and better estimates for π. Archimedes found that π was between $\frac{223}{71}$ and $\frac{22}{7}$. This process is described in Archimedes' *Measurement of a Circle.* Today, we often use either $\frac{22}{7}$ or 3.14 as estimates for π.

Historical Note

In 1767, Johann Heinrich Lambert showed that π is an irrational number, that is, a number that cannot be expressed as a ratio of integers. An irrational number has a nonterminating, nonrepeating decimal part. Thus, any calculation of π is only an approximation, no matter how many digits are involved. Mathematicians have found more and more of the digits in the decimal expression for π. In 1986, the NASA Ames Research Center used a supercomputer to find the value of π to 29,360,000 digits. It took the computer 28 hours to produce this estimate for π. In 1999, π was computed to over 200 billion decimal digits.

Figure 1: *Inscribed and circumscribed polygons about a circle*

Geometry Tools

Students come to realize that the tools (compass and straightedge) that were available to Archimedes around 240 BCE to measure and calculate π are the same tools that they will use. While the compass and the straightedge are still powerful tools for teaching students geometry, geometric constructions are now often explored using computers.

In Lessons 3 and 4, students learn to use a compass and straightedge (ruler) and then apply this knowledge to construct various shapes. Using a compass and ruler gives students the opportunity to learn more about geometric shapes and reinforces previously learned ideas. For example, in Unit 6, children using chenille sticks found that three lengths

uniquely determine a triangle. In this unit, they use a compass and ruler to construct triangles, given the lengths of the three sides. Children also revisit the idea that two sides and the included angle also uniquely determine a triangle. Doing constructions helps children learn more about the figures they are constructing, and it also gives them a new mathematical tool. Finally, being introduced to the compass gives students an interesting historical perspective on the development of mathematics.

The activities in this unit, like other geometry units, aim to develop students' spatial sense. Research indicates that spatial ability is positively correlated with mathematics achievement at all grade levels (Fennema and Sherman, 1978; Guay and McDaniel, 1977).

Resources

*   Beckmann, Petr. *A History of π (Pi)*. St. Martin's Press, New York, 1971.
*   Clements, Douglas H., and Michael T. Battista. "Geometry and Spatial Reasoning." In *Handbook for Research on Mathematics Teaching and Learning,* Douglas A. Grouws (ed.). Macmillan Publishing Company, New York, 1992.
*   Eves, Howard. *An Introduction to the History of Mathematics.* Harcourt Brace Jovanovich, New York, 1992.
*   Fennema, E., and J. Sherman. "Sex-Related Differences in Mathematics Achievement and Related Factors." *Journal for Research in Mathematics Education,* 9, pp. 189–203, 1978.
*   Fuys, D., D. Geddes, and R. Tischer. "The van Hiele Model of Thinking in Geometry Among Adolescents." *Journal for Research in Mathematics Education Monograph,* 3, 1988.
*   Guay, R.B., and E. McDaniel. "The Relationship between Mathematics Achievement and Spatial Abilities among Elementary School Children." *Journal for Research in Mathematics Education,* 8, pp. 211–215, 1977.

Assessment Indicators

*   Can students identify the parts of a circle?
*   Can students express the relationship between the circumference and diameter of a circle using words and symbols?
*   Can students use variables in formulas?
*   Can students measure length in centimeters?
*   Can students collect, organize, graph, and analyze data?
*   Can students draw and interpret best-fit lines?
*   Can students use words, tables, graphs, and fractions to express ratios?
*   Can students use fractions, decimals, and percents to represent the same quantity?
*   Can students construct geometric figures using rulers, compasses, and protractors?
*   Can students make and interpret circle graphs?

OBSERVATIONAL ASSESSMENT RECORD

(A1) Can students identify the parts of a circle?

(A2) Can students express the relationship between the circumference and diameter of a circle using words and symbols?

(A3) Can students use variables in formulas?

(A4) Can students measure length in centimeters?

(A5) Can students collect, organize, graph, and analyze data?

(A6) Can students draw and interpret best-fit lines?

(A7) Can students use words, tables, graphs, and fractions to express ratios?

(A8) Can students use fractions, decimals, and percents to represent the same quantity?

(A9) Can students construct geometric figures using rulers, compasses, and protractors?

(A10) Can students make and interpret circle graphs?

Name	A1	A2	A3	A4	A5	A6	A7	A8	A9	A10	Comments
1.											
2.											
3.											
4.											
5.											
6.											
7.											
8.											
9.											
10.											
11.											
12.											
13.											

Name	A1	A2	A3	A4	A5	A6	A7	A8	A9	A10	Comments
14.											
15.											
16.											
17.											
18.											
19.											
20.											
21.											
22.											
23.											
24.											
25.											
26.											
27.											
28.											
29.											
30.											
31.											
32.											

Daily Practice and Problems

Using Circles

A DPP Menu for Unit 14

Eight icons are used to designate the subject matter of the DPP items. Each DPP item may fall into one or more of the categories listed below. The icons appear in the Teacher Notes column in each of the DPP items. Below is a brief menu of the DPP items included in Unit 14.

N Number Sense	**✖** Computation	**◷** Time	**⊟** Geometry
C, D, F, H, L–T	B–D, F, I, J, L, N–T	A	I, M, U, V
Math Facts	**$** Money	**Measurement**	**Data**
E, G, K, O, P, S, W		I, M, U	F, X

Two DPP items are included for each class session listed in the Unit Outline. The first item is always a Bit and the second is either a Task or a Challenge. The *Daily Practice and Problems and Home Practice Guide* in the *Teacher Implementation Guide* includes information on how and when to use the DPP. A *Scope and Sequence Chart* for the Daily Practice and Problems for the year can also be found in the *Teacher Implementation Guide*.

Review and Assessment of Math Facts

By the end of fourth grade, students in *Math Trailblazers™* are expected to demonstrate fluency with all the division facts. The DPP for this unit continues the systematic approach to reviewing the division facts. This unit reviews the related division facts for the 3s and the 9s. This unit also reviews the related division facts in the group of multiplication facts known as the last six facts. Since there are two related division facts for each multiplication fact, there are 12 division facts in this group ($24 \div 6 = 4$, $24 \div 4 = 6$, $28 \div 4 = 7$, $28 \div 7 = 4$, $32 \div 8 = 4$, $32 \div 4 = 8$, $42 \div 6 = 7$, $42 \div 7 = 6$, $48 \div 6 = 8$, $48 \div 8 = 6$, $56 \div 8 = 7$, $56 \div 7 = 8$).

For more information about the distribution and assessment of the math facts, see the TIMS Tutor: *Math Facts* in the *Teacher Implementation Guide* and the *Grade 5 Facts Resource Guide*.

14 Daily Practice and Problems

Students may solve the items individually, in groups, or as a class. The items may also be assigned for homework.

Student Questions	Teacher Notes
A **Scheduling Activities**	**TIMS Bit**
Ms. Internet schedules the following times for each of three activities she wants her students to complete at the computer. How many minutes are assigned for each activity?	1. 66 minutes 2. 22 minutes 3. 23 minutes
1. Word processing: 8:48 to 9:54 A.M.	
2. Graphing data from an experiment: 9:55 to 10:17 A.M.	
3. Geography game: 10:20 to 10:43 A.M.	
B **Division Practice**	**TIMS Task**
Use paper and pencil or mental math to solve the following division problems. Write any remainders as fractions in lowest terms. Estimate to be sure your answers are reasonable.	A. $11\frac{1}{2}$ B. $508\frac{2}{3}$ C. 60 D. $73\frac{1}{2}$ E. $50\frac{1}{5}$ F. 200
A. $138 \div 12 =$	
B. $4578 \div 9 =$	
C. $600 \div 10 =$	
D. $588 \div 8 =$	
E. $1004 \div 20 =$	
F. $1000 \div 5 =$	

Student Questions	Teacher Notes

 C **Compute Mentally**

Find the answers to the following without using paper and pencil or a calculator.

A. $0.8 \times 50 =$ B. $0.9 \times 0.5 =$

C. $5.0 \times 0.7 =$ D. $0.3 \times 0.3 =$

E. $3.0 \times 0.8 =$ F. $0.1 \times 0.06 =$

TIMS Bit

A. 40	B. 0.45
C. 3.5	D. 0.09
E. 2.4	F. 0.006

D **Fractions** *Digits Game*

Draw boxes like these on your paper.

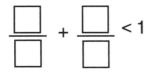

As your teacher or classmate chooses 4 digits from a deck of 6 digit cards, place them in the boxes. Try to make the sum of the two fractions as close to one as possible, but not equal to or greater than one. Remember that each digit can be chosen only once. Once you place a digit, it cannot be moved.

TIMS Task

To begin the game, students draw the set of boxes on their paper. The teacher makes a set of 6 digit cards using the numbers 1, 2, 3, 4, 6, and 8. The teacher chooses one digit at random from the set of cards. Students place the digit in a box in such a way as to try to get a sum of two fractions that is closest to, but less than, 1. Once a digit is placed, it cannot be moved. The teacher chooses a second digit without replacing the first in the deck. Play continues until the teacher has read enough digits to fill the boxes. Students can use calculators to compare their sums. If one student has $\frac{1}{4} + \frac{3}{6}$, the student can press on a scientific calculator: $1 \div 4 + 3 \div 6 =$ to get 0.75. Another student can solve $\frac{1}{6} + \frac{2}{3}$ by pressing $1 \div 6 + 2 \div 3 =$. This student gets 0.8333333. By comparing the decimal answers, the students can see who is the winner.

Student Questions	Teacher Notes

 Division Fact Practice

A. 21 ÷ 7 =

B. 63 ÷ 9 =

C. 48 ÷ 8 =

D. 12 ÷ 4 =

E. 32 ÷ 4 =

F. 30 ÷ 10 =

G. 45 ÷ 5 =

H. 18 ÷ 9 =

TIMS Bit

A. 3   B. 7

C. 6   D. 3

E. 8   F. 3

G. 9   H. 2

 Spilled Ink

Professor Peabody spilled some ink on his *Circumference vs. Diameter* data table. Solve for the numbers that are covered in ink.

TIMS Task

Small Trial 2: 9.6 cm

Medium Mean: 28.8 cm

Large Trial 1: 39.7 cm

D Circle in ___cm___	C in ___cm___			
	Trial 1	Trial 2	Trial 3	Mean
small	3	9.5	(ink)	9.7	9.6
medium	9.2	28.8	28.8	28.9	(ink)
large	12.6	(ink)	39.6	39.5	39.6

 Division Fact Practice

A. 560 ÷ 80 =

B. 180 ÷ 30 =

C. 280 ÷ 70 =

D. 7200 ÷ 80 =

E. 6000 ÷ 300 =

F. 240 ÷ 80 =

G. 360 ÷ 40 =

H. 900 ÷ 30 =

TIMS Bit

A. 7   B. 6

C. 4   D. 90

E. 20   F. 3

G. 9   H. 30

Student Questions	Teacher Notes

 Multiples of 2 and 4

Irma studies the multiples of 4 and notices that 48, 40, 20, 16, and 32 are all divisible by 2 as well as 4. Therefore, Irma believes all numbers that are divisible by 2 must also be divisible by 4. Is Irma correct in her thinking? Explain.

TIMS Task

Irma is incorrect. It only requires one counterexample to show her thinking is incorrect. 22 is divisible by 2 but not by 4.

 Quiz: Try Some Pi

Solve the following problems using the π key on your calculator. Give your answers to the nearest tenth of a centimeter.

1. If the diameter of a circle is 4 cm, what is the circumference?

2. If the radius is 3.5 cm, what is the circumference?

3. If the circumference is 8 cm, what is the diameter?

4. If the circumference is 18 cm, what is the radius?

TIMS Bit

1. 12.6 cm
2. 22.0 cm
3. 2.5 cm
4. 2.9 cm

Function Machine

Here is a machine that takes the input number, multiplies it by 4, and subtracts 1 from the product. Thus, the rule for this machine is $N \times 4 - 1$. Complete the table for this function machine.

Input N	Output
1	3
2	
6	
7	
8	
	39
12	
13	
	71
20	

TIMS Task

Input N	Output
1	3
2	7
6	23
7	27
8	31
10	39
12	47
13	51
18	71
20	79

 Division Fact Practice

A. $81 \div 9 = n$ B. $42 \div n = 7$

C. $n \div 3 = 9$ D. $n \div 6 = 4$

E. $15 \div n = 3$ F. $54 \div 6 = n$

TIMS Bit

A. 9   B. 6

C. 27   D. 24

E. 5   F. 9

Student Questions	Teacher Notes

Computation Practice

Solve the following using paper and pencil. Estimate to be sure your answers are reasonable.

A. $28,468 \div 4 =$ B. $6243 - 4139 =$

C. $94 \times 24 =$ D. $3467 + 9246 =$

E. $346 \times 0.3 =$ F. $8.7 \times 0.23 =$

TIMS Task

A. 7117	B. 2104
C. 2256	D. 12,713
E. 103.8	F. 2.001

Which Is Larger?

Which has a larger face:

A circular watch face that has a diameter of 3 cm or one that has a circumference of 9 cm? Explain how you know.

TIMS Bit

The watch that has a diameter of 3 cm has a larger face. The circumference of a circle is always a little more than 3 times the diameter. Thus, the circumference of the circle with diameter 3 cm will be greater than 9 cm.

What's My Rule?

Find the rule for this function machine. Then, use the rule to complete the table.

Input N	Output
0	1
2	5
5	11
8	
	21
	41

TIMS Challenge

$N \times 2 + 1 =$ output

Input N	Output
0	1
2	5
5	11
8	17
10	21
20	41

Student Questions	Teacher Notes

 Division

A. $3200 \div 80 =$

B. $63,000 \div 70 =$

C. $210 \div 3 =$

D. $480 \div 60 =$

E. $5400 \div 900 =$

F. $2400 \div 4 =$

TIMS Bit

A. 40

B. 900

C. 70

D. 8

E. 6

F. 600

P Prime Factors

Write each of the following numbers as a product of primes using exponents. Use factor trees to organize your work.

A. 3600

B. 2800

C. 4500

TIMS Task

Have students share their strategies. One way to start the factor trees is to think of the facts. $3600 = 60 \times 60$ or 40×90. Likewise, $2800 = 40 \times 70$ and $4500 = 90 \times 50$. Another way is to factor out 100 first and begin with 36×100, 28×100, and 45×100.

A. $2^4 \times 3^2 \times 5^2$

B. $2^4 \times 5^2 \times 7$

C. $2^2 \times 5^3 \times 3^2$

Q Multiplying Fractions

Multiply using mental math whenever possible.

1. A. $\frac{1}{8} \times 16 =$ B. $\frac{3}{4} \times 12 =$

   C. $\frac{1}{10} \times 20 =$ D. $\frac{4}{5} \times 25 =$

   E. $33 \times \frac{1}{3} =$ F. $\frac{1}{8} \times \frac{8}{10} =$

2. Explain your strategy for 1D.

TIMS Bit

1. A. 2   B. 9

   C. 2   D. 20

   E. 11   F. $\frac{1}{10}$

2. $\frac{1}{5}$ of 25 is 5, so

   $\frac{4}{5}$ of 25 is 4×5 or 20.

Shirts

A closet has 20 shirts.

1. $\frac{1}{5}$ of the shirts are dress shirts. How many dress shirts are in the closet?

2. $\frac{1}{2}$ of the dress shirts are white.

 A. How many shirts are white dress shirts?

 B. What fraction of the shirts in the closet are white dress shirts?

3. $\frac{1}{2}$ of the shirts are work shirts. How many work shirts are in the closet?

4. The rest of the shirts are t-shirts. What fraction of the shirts are t-shirts?

TIMS Task

Encourage students to draw a picture to help them solve the problems if they are stuck.

1. 4 dress shirts

2. A. 2 white dress shirts

 B. $\frac{2}{20}$ or $\frac{1}{10}$

3. 10 work shirts

4. 6 shirts; $\frac{6}{20}$ or $\frac{3}{10}$

 Division

Solve the following using mental math.

A. $30 \div 8 =$

B. $40 \div 9 =$

C. $45 \div 6 =$

D. $15 \div 4 =$

E. $34 \div 7 =$

F. $62 \div 8 =$

TIMS Bit

A. 3 R6

B. 4 R4

C. 7 R3

D. 3 R3

E. 4 R6

F. 7 R6

Fractions and Mixed Numbers

1. Rewrite each of the following as mixed numbers with no improper fractions. All fractions should be in lowest terms.

   A. $8\frac{10}{6}$

   B. $\frac{27}{6}$

   C. $3\frac{9}{4}$

   D. $\frac{88}{12}$

2. A. $3\frac{1}{8} + 7\frac{2}{3} =$

   B. $4\frac{5}{6} + 1\frac{5}{12} =$

   C. $8\frac{13}{16} + 2\frac{1}{2} =$

1. A. $9\frac{4}{6} = 9\frac{2}{3}$

   B. $4\frac{3}{6} = 4\frac{1}{2}$

   C. $5\frac{1}{4}$

   D. $7\frac{4}{12} = 7\frac{1}{3}$

2. A. $10\frac{19}{24}$

   B. $6\frac{3}{12} = 6\frac{1}{4}$

   C. $11\frac{5}{16}$

 Constructions

TIMS Bit

1. Draw a circle O with a diameter of 8 cm.

2. Draw a chord. Label it EF.

3. Draw a radius. Label it OT.

4. Draw a central angle. Label it BOV.

Students will need compasses and rulers. Constructions will vary. One solution is provided here.

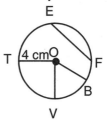

Coordinate Geometry

The vertices of triangle PQR have the following coordinates:

P is at (4, 3)   Q is at (-1, -1)   R is at (3, -2)

True or false:

1. If the triangle slides 5 units to the right, the *y*-coordinate of P' will be 8.

2. If the triangle slides 4 units down, the *x*-coordinate of Q' will be -1.

3. If the triangle is flipped over the *y*-axis, the *y*-coordinates of P', Q', and R' will stay the same.

4. If the triangle slides 3 units to the left and 3 units down, the *x*- and *y*-coordinates of P', Q', and R' will all be negative.

TIMS Challenge

Assign this item to students who completed the optional lessons on flips and slides in Unit 10 Lessons 6 and 7.

Students can plot triangle PQR on a piece of *Centimeter Grid Paper*. In order to answer the questions they can perform the slides and flips indicated.

1. False; The *x*-coordinate will be 9. The *y*-coordinate remains 3.

2. True

3. True

4. False; The coordinates of P' would be (1, 0). You have to slide the triangle 5 units to the left and 4 units down for the *x*- and *y*-coordinates of P', Q', and R' to all be negative.

Division Fact Practice

A. 48 ÷ 8 =

B. 6 ÷ 2 =

C. 72 ÷ 9 =

D. 32 ÷ 4 =

E. 54 ÷ 9 =

F. 90 ÷ 9 =

G. 30 ÷ 3 =

H. 45 ÷ 9 =

I. 28 ÷ 4 =

J. 18 ÷ 3 =

K. 24 ÷ 3 =

L. 9 ÷ 3 =

M. 42 ÷ 7 =

N. 18 ÷ 9 =

O. 81 ÷ 9 =

P. 12 ÷ 4 =

Q. 63 ÷ 9 =

R. 21 ÷ 3 =

S. 15 ÷ 3 =

T. 56 ÷ 7 =

U. 27 ÷ 3 =

V. 36 ÷ 9 =

W. 24 ÷ 6 =

TIMS Bit

A. 6

B. 3

C. 8

D. 8

E. 6

F. 10

G. 10

H. 5

I. 7

J. 6

K. 8

L. 3

M. 6

N. 2

O. 9

P. 3

Q. 7

R. 3

S. 5

T. 8

U. 9

V. 4

W. 4

Logic at a National Park

Felicia, Brandon, and Ana visited the
National Park on a field trip. Each liked best
a different activity at the park (movie, fossil
collection, or the nature display). Each liked
a different location at the park (the quarry,
the excavation, or the river bluff). Each
bought a different lunch (chili, hamburger,
or soup). Read these clues to see who liked
what best.

A. Brandon bought a hamburger, and
    Ana enjoyed the movie.

B. The girl who loved fossils and the
    girl who liked the quarry talked to the
    park ranger.

C. The girl who ate chili and the girl
    who liked the bluff wrote notes in
    their books.

TIMS Challenge

Discuss students' strategies.

Felicia—fossil, river bluff, soup

Brandon—display, excavation, hamburger

Ana—movie, quarry, chili

A. Scheduling Activities (URG p. 10)

Ms. Internet schedules the following times for each of three activities she wants her students to complete at the computer. How many minutes are assigned for each activity?

1. Word processing: 8:48 to 9:54 A.M.

2. Graphing data from an experiment: 9:55 to 10:17 A.M.

3. Geography game: 10:20 to 10:43 A.M.

DPP Task is on page 27. Suggestions for using the DPPs are on page 27.

LESSON GUIDE

Exploring Circumference and Diameter

> Estimated Class Sessions: 1

Students explore the relationship between the circumference and the diameter of circles by estimating their measurements with string. They find that the circumference of a circle is equal to about three times the diameter.

Key Content

- Identifying the parts of a circle.
- Investigating the relationship between circumference and diameter.

Key Vocabulary

center
circle
circumference
diameter
perimeter

Curriculum Sequence

Before This Unit

In Units 2 and 16 of fourth grade, students studied the perimeter of polygons.

Materials List

Print Materials for Students

		Math Facts and Daily Practice and Problems	Activity	Homework
Student Books	Student Guide		*Exploring Circumference and Diameter* Pages 426–427	
	Discovery Assignment Book			*Gluing It Down* Page 213 and Home Practice Part 1 Page 209
Teacher Resource	Unit Resource Guide	DPP Items A–B Page 10 ⊙		

⊙ *available on Teacher Resource CD*

All Transparency Masters, Blackline Masters, and Assessment Blackline Masters in the Unit Resource Guide are on the Teacher Resource CD.

Supplies for Each Student Pair

2 lengths of string that do not stretch, approximately 5 feet long
glue
scissors
2–3 cans and lids of various sizes

Student Guide - Page 426

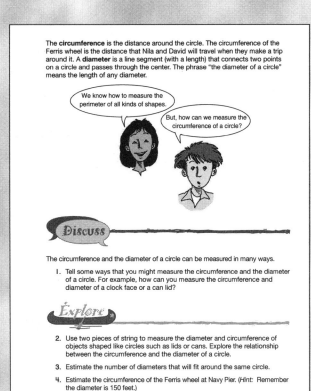

Student Guide - Page 427

Before the Activity

Organize various circular objects so each pair of students measures 2 or 3.

Developing the Activity

Introduce students to the idea of measuring circles or circular-shaped objects and the terminology associated with circles using the first page of the *Exploring Circumference and Diameter* Activity Pages. Nila and David are interested in the Ferris wheel at Navy Pier in Chicago. As of 1997, the Ferris wheel at Navy Pier is the largest in the world. It is 150 feet in height and can hold up to 240 people in its 40 gondolas.

Show students the circumference and the diameter of a circle on the first page as they read the definitions on the second page. Make sure that students understand that every diameter has the same length. Students should be familiar with the word perimeter. Discuss that the circumference is the perimeter of a circle. If students have difficulty seeing that the circumference of a circle is a length, demonstrate the length with a trundle wheel or a piece of string.

Content Note

Circles. In everyday language, a **circle** means a plane region bounded by a single curved line, every point of which is equally distant from the point at the **center** of the figure. It can also mean the boundary of such a figure. In mathematics, we use the latter meaning. It is a curve, not a region. The **circumference** of a circle can mean either the curve boundary of a circle (i.e., the circle itself) or the distance around the circle. **A diameter** of a circle is any line segment connecting two points on the circle and passing through the center. **The diameter** is the length of any diameter.

Question 1 asks students how they might measure the circumference and the diameter of circles. The diameter can be measured using a ruler, but measuring the circumference is a bit more difficult. Students might suggest using a tape measure that bends, estimating with their rulers, or laying a string around the circumference and then measuring the length of the string. All of these methods are satisfactory, but some are more accurate than others.

Students will use only string in this activity to get a sense of the relationship between the circumference and the diameter of a circle. They will compare the length of string that measures the circumference to the length of the string that measures the diameter.

More exact methods for measuring the circumference of a circle are explored in the lab *Circumference vs. Diameter* in Lesson 2.

 **TIMS Tip**

To develop an intuitive understanding of circles, choose a student to be the center. Choose 10 other students and tell them to stand 1 meter from the center. These 10 students will form (part of) a circle.

Encourage students to list the circles or circular-shaped objects that they see. Discuss the fact that the circular-shaped objects in the classroom are three-dimensional, but that students are really just interested in the two-dimensional circles shown. Make a list of the objects on the chalkboard. Some possibilities are:

- a circular clock face
- a circular rim of the trash can
- a coffee can cylinder
- circular lids to containers
- a circular table
- a circular opening of a pot for a plant
- a film canister
- spools of thread
- masking tape rolls
- soup cans
- wheels on a wheelchair or carts

Choose one of the objects and hold it so that the class can see it. Discuss the appropriate place to measure the circumference and the diameter of the object. If a can has grooves or dents, for example, these are not good places to measure the circumference.

Assign pairs of students several circular objects to measure. Try to vary the size of the objects. Give each pair of students two lengths of string. Ask pairs to measure and explore the circumference and diameter of their circles with the string *(Question 2)*.

TIMS Tip

Use string that does not stretch too much, or it will make it more difficult for students to recognize the relationship between circumference and the diameter.

One student should measure the diameter, while the other measures the circumference. If students have difficulty measuring the circumference, have one partner hold the end of the string on the object, while the

other wraps it around. Measurements for the diameter should go through the widest part of the circle. Pairs should then hold up their lengths of string and compare them as shown in Figure 2 *(Question 3)*.

One student measures circumference.

One student measures diameter.

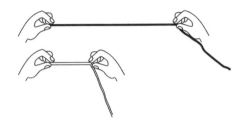
Students compare the lengths of the strings.

Figure 2: *Finding the relationship between the circumference and diameter of a circle*

Have students cut off the extra string to show the lengths. They can then lay these lengths down and compare them side by side. Students may need to fold the length of the circumference into thirds to verify that the circumference is indeed about three times the diameter.

After students have measured and made their estimates, discuss the relationship between the two lengths of string. With all the information from the class, students should see that the circumference is about three times longer than the diameter. The relationship between the circumference and the diameter does not change, no matter how large or small the circle. There are always about three diameters in the circumference.

Once student pairs have explored a variety of circles and have discovered the relationship, encourage them to answer *Question 4.* They can estimate that the circumference of the Ferris wheel is 3×150 feet or 450 feet.

Explain to students that the relationship they explored is only an approximation. You might want to discuss with students whether the actual relationship is more or less than three. This discussion will make a transition into Lesson 2.

Suggestions for Teaching the Lesson

Homework and Practice

- Assign the *Gluing It Down* Homework Page in the *Discovery Assignment Book.* This activity reinforces the idea that the circumference of a circle is always about three times the diameter.

- Assign DPP Bit A which practices elapsed time and DPP Task B which practices paper-and-pencil division.

- Assign Part 1 of the Home Practice which practices paper-and-pencil division.

Answers for Part 1 of the Home Practice can be found in the Answer Key at the end of this lesson and at the end of this unit.

Extension

Tack students' lengths for the circumference and the diameter for a variety of circles on a bulletin board. Label the strings appropriately as circumference or diameter. This will further reinforce students' understanding that the circumference of a circle is always about three times the diameter—regardless of the size of the circle.

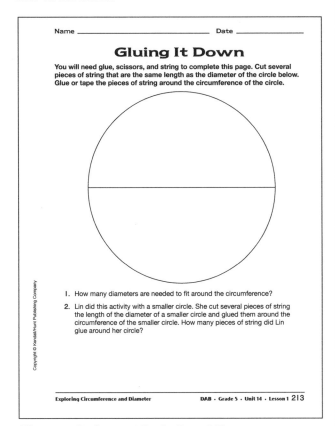

Gluing It Down

You will need glue, scissors, and string to complete this page. Cut several pieces of string that are the same length as the diameter of the circle below. Glue or tape the pieces of string around the circumference of the circle.

1. How many diameters are needed to fit around the circumference?

2. Lin did this activity with a smaller circle. She cut several pieces of string the length of the diameter of a smaller circle and glued them around the circumference of the smaller circle. How many pieces of string did Lin glue around her circle?

Name _____ Date _____

Exploring Circumference and Diameter   DAB · Grade 5 · Unit 14 · Lesson 1 213

***Discovery Assignment Book* - Page 213**

Daily Practice and Problems: Task for Lesson 1

B. Task: Division Practice (URG p. 10)

Use paper and pencil or mental math to solve the following division problems. Write any remainders as fractions in lowest terms. Estimate to be sure your answers are reasonable.

A. $138 \div 12 =$

B. $4578 \div 9 =$

C. $600 \div 10 =$

D. $588 \div 8 =$

E. $1004 \div 20 =$

F. $1000 \div 5 =$

Name _____ Date _____

Unit 14: Home Practice

Part 1 Division Practice

Use paper and pencil or mental math to solve the following problems. Estimate to be sure your answers are reasonable. Explain your estimation strategy for A.

A. $8965 \div 57 =$ B. $7682 \div 40 =$ C. $4128 \div 4 \div 2 =$

D. $4128 \div 8 =$ E. $7900 \div 10 =$

Part 2 Order of Operations

Solve the following problems following the order of operations. Use paper and pencil or mental math.

A. $18 \div 3 \times 7 =$ B. $15 + 24 \div 4 =$ C. $350 - 210 \div 7 =$

D. $60 + 80 \times 7 =$ E. $7^2 \times 2^2 =$ F. $30 \times 80 \div 6 =$

G. $60 \times 80 + 1200 =$ H. $4500 \div 9 - 5 =$ I. $(130 + 150) \div 4 =$

USING CIRCLES   DAB · Grade 5 · Unit 14 209

***Discovery Assignment Book* - Page 209**

AT A GLANCE

Math Facts and Daily Practice and Problems

DPP item A reviews elapsed time. Task B reviews paper-and-pencil division.

Developing the Activity

1. Students learn about the circumference and diameter of circles using the *Exploring Circumference and Diameter* Activity Pages in the *Student Guide.*
2. Students discuss how they might measure the circumference and the diameter of circles. *(Question 1)*
3. Students identify circles in the classroom.
4. Student pairs measure and compare the diameter and circumference of circles. *(Question 2)*
5. Student pairs find the approximate relationship between the circumference and the diameter of circles. *(Questions 3–4)*

Homework

1. Assign the *Gluing It Down* Homework Page in the *Discovery Assignment Book.*
2. Assign Part 1 of the Home Practice.

Notes:

Student Guide

Questions 1–4 (SG p. 427)

I. *Answers will vary. Possible responses include the following. The diameter can be measured using a ruler. The circumference can be measured by laying a string around the circle and then measuring the length of the string, or by using a tape measure that bends.

2–3. *Answers will vary. There are always about 3 diameters in the circumference of a circle.

4. The circumference of the Ferris wheel ≈ $3 \times 150 = 450$ feet.

Discovery Assignment Book

**Home Practice (DAB p. 209)

Part 1. Division Practice

Questions A–E

A. 157 R16; One possible strategy for estimation: $10,000 \div 50 = 200$.

B. $192\frac{1}{20}$ or 192 R2

C. 516

D. 516

E. 790

Gluing It Down (DAB p. 213)

Questions 1–2

Check that each student has three pieces of string glued about the circumference. Each piece of string should be the length of the diameter.

I. About 3

2. 3

---

*Answers and/or discussion are included in the Lesson Guide.

**Answers for all the Home Practice in the *Discovery Assignment Book* are at the end of the unit.

LESSON GUIDE 2

Circumference vs. Diameter

Estimated Class Sessions: 3–4

Students measure the circumference and diameter of circles to improve their understanding of the relationship between the circumference and diameter of a circle. They record their measurements in a data table, plot them on a graph, and analyze their results. Students learn that the circumference of a circle is equal to π times the diameter.

Key Content

- Measuring length.
- Finding and expressing the relationship between the circumference and the diameter of circles: $C = \pi \times D$.
- Defining π as the ratio of circumference to diameter of a circle.
- Collecting, organizing, graphing, and analyzing data.
- Drawing and interpreting best-fit lines.
- Using words, tables, graphs, and fractions to express ratios.
- Using variables in formulas.
- Solving problems involving circles.
- Using fractions, decimals, and percents to represent the same quantity.

Key Vocabulary

extrapolation
formula
interpolation
π (pi)

Curriculum Sequence

Before This Unit

Students used straight lines on graphs to find equal ratios in several activities including the laboratory investigations *Distance vs. Time* in Unit 3, *Spreading Out* in Unit 4, and *Mass vs. Volume* in Unit 13.

Materials List

DORDT COLLEGE
JOHN AND LOUISE HULST LIBRARY
SIOUX CENTER, IOWA 51250

Print Materials for Students

		Math Facts and Daily Practice and Problems	Lab	Homework	Written Assessment
Student Books	**Student Guide**		*Circumference vs. Diameter* Pages 428–433	*Circumference vs. Diameter* Homework Section Pages 433–434	
	Discovery Assignment Book			Home Practice Parts 2 & 3 Pages 209–210	
Teacher Resources	**Facts Resource Guide** ⊙	DPP Items 14E and 14G			
	Unit Resource Guide ⊙	DPP Items C–H Pages 11–13 ⊙			*Going Around in Circles* Page 41, 1 per student
	Generic Section ⊙		*Centimeter Graph Paper* and *Three-trial Data Table*, 1 each per student		

⊙ *available on Teacher Resource CD*

All Transparency Masters, Blackline Masters, and Assessment Blackline Masters in the Unit Resource Guide are on the Teacher Resource CD.

Supplies for Each Student

cans and circular lids of various sizes
centimeter ruler
string that will not stretch, or adding machine tape
calculator

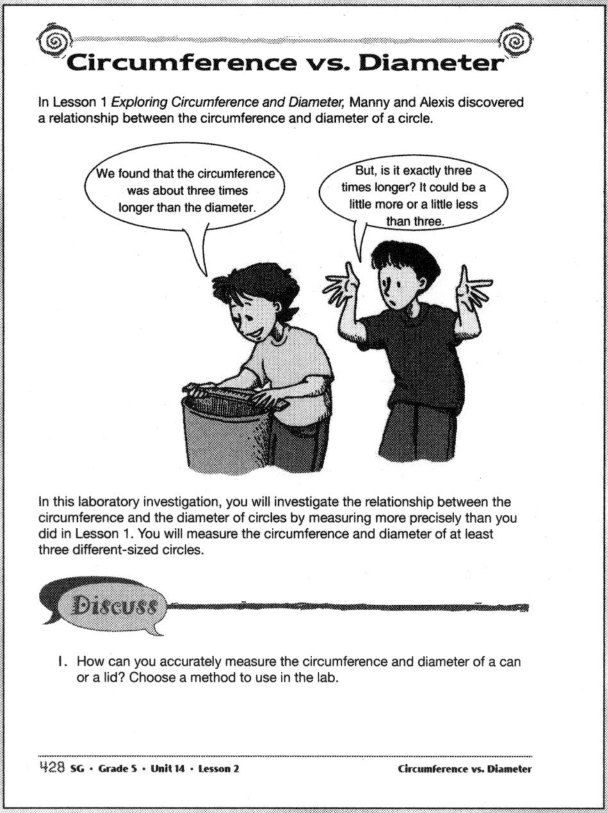

Circumference vs. Diameter

In Lesson 1 *Exploring Circumference and Diameter,* Manny and Alexis discovered a relationship between the circumference and diameter of a circle.

We found that the circumference was about three times longer than the diameter.
But, is it exactly three times longer? It could be a little more or a little less than three.

In this laboratory investigation, you will investigate the relationship between the circumference and the diameter of circles by measuring more precisely than you did in Lesson 1. You will measure the circumference and diameter of at least three different-sized circles.

Discuss

1. How can you accurately measure the circumference and diameter of a can or a lid? Choose a method to use in the lab.

428 SG • Grade 5 • Unit 14 • Lesson 2 Circumference vs. Diameter

Student Guide **- Page 428**

Before the Activity

A good selection of circular objects for students to measure includes empty spools of thread or film canisters for small objects, soup cans or masking tape rolls for medium objects, and coffee cans or large lids for large objects. Ask students to bring these objects to school.

Developing the Activity

Part 1. Beginning the Investigation and Drawing the Picture

In Lesson 1 *Exploring Circumference and Diameter,* students found that the circumference of a circle is equal to about three diameters. A vignette on the first *Circumference vs. Diameter* Activity Page in the *Student Guide* reviews this idea.

During this investigation, students will carefully measure the diameter *(D)* and the circumference *(C)* of at least three different-sized circles. They will record their information in a table, graph the data, and then look for the relationship between the two variables: circumference and diameter. We use cans or jar lids as our circles, since they are easier to measure than a circle drawn on paper.

Begin a discussion about how students might refine their estimates for the relationship between circumference and diameter. Emphasize that in order to improve their estimates they will need to measure with accuracy. ***Question 1*** in the *Student Guide* asks them to list their ideas. Some possible ways to measure the circumference and diameter follow:

- Use a ruler to measure the diameter.
- Use a string to measure the circumference and diameter. Then, measure the string with a ruler to the nearest tenth of a centimeter. (It is important to use string that does not stretch so the measurement will be accurate.)
- Roll a can along a piece of paper until it completes one revolution. Mark the beginning of the roll and the end of the roll on the paper. Then, measure the distance between the marks to find the circumference. Students should mark their starting point on the can with a piece of tape or a pen mark, so they know when they have completed one revolution. If this method is used, emphasize the importance of rolling the can in a straight path. Cans have a tendency to slide which makes the data less accurate. See Figure 3.

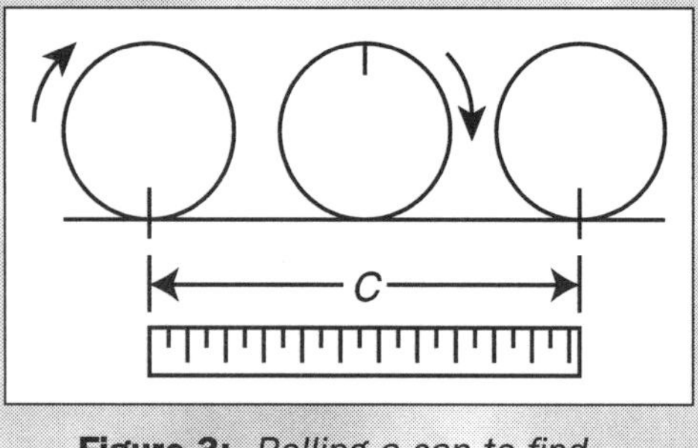

C

Figure 3: *Rolling a can to find its circumference*

- Wrap adding machine tape around the can or lid and mark the start and end points to measure the circumference. Students will find it easier to mark the start and the end points if they lay the can on its side. See Figure 4.

When measuring the diameter of a circle, students must make sure that their ruler crosses through the center of the circle. On some lids, there may be a small point in the plastic that designates the center. If students are using circles that do not have a designated center, instruct them to find the longest length that connects opposite sides of the circle. They may need to take a couple of measurements to be sure they found the longest length. This length is the diameter.

Have students discuss techniques for measuring their particular cans or lids. For example, a coffee can may have grooves so they should not take a measurement for the circumference in a groove because the circumference of that circle does not correspond to the diameter measured at the top of the can. In all cases, students need to measure the circumference of the circle that corresponds to the diameter they measured.

Tell student pairs that they will measure the circumference and diameter of at least three different-sized cans or lids in this investigation. They will measure a small, a medium, and a large circle. Discuss with students that although they may be measuring three-dimensional objects, they are really interested in just the circle, which is two-dimensional. Students should use the same method to measure all three circles. Using the same measurement method helps to minimize experimental error.

Once students are familiar with the measurement procedure they will use, encourage them to draw a picture of the investigation *(Question 2)*. Students should identify the variables in their drawings. See Figure 5 for a sample picture.

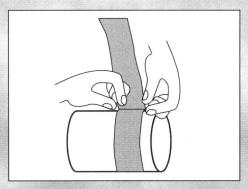

Figure 4: *Wrapping adding machine tape to measure the circumference*

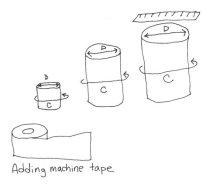

Figure 5: *Sample picture of the lab*

2. Draw a picture that shows your experiment. Your picture should show the method you chose to measure the circumference and the diameter. Label the circumference *C* and the diameter *D*.

Take your measurements from at least three different-sized cans or lids.

3. A. Measure the diameter for each circle to the nearest tenth of a centimeter. Compare your measurements to your partner's measurements. Agree on the length of the diameter for each circle, then record the value in a table similar to the one shown below.

   B. Measure the circumference of each circle to the nearest tenth of a centimeter three times. Record each of your measurements in a table similar to the one shown below.

Circle	*D* in ____	*C* in ____			
		Trial 1	Trial 2	Trial 3	Mean
Small					
Medium					
Large					

4. Use a calculator to find the mean circumference for each size can or lid and record it in your data table. Find the mean to the nearest tenth of a cm.

5. Why is it a good idea to do more than one trial and find a mean value for the circumference of each can or lid?

Student Guide - Page 429

Content Note

Unit 4 Lesson 4 *How Close Is Close Enough?* is an optional lesson that teaches students how to use 10% as a standard for error analysis. Students who completed this lesson can use these skills to check to see if their measurements for the circumference of a circle are within 10% of one another.

If students have not completed this lesson, they should understand that all the measurements for a given circumference should be relatively close. For more information, see the TIMS Tutor: *Estimation, Accuracy, and Error.*

Part 2. Collecting the Data

Student pairs should carefully measure the diameter of each circle to the nearest tenth of a centimeter *(Question 3A)*. To ensure that pairs have found the best measurements for the diameter, each partner should measure the diameter. Partners can then compare their measurements to see if they are accurate. If the measurements differ, each partner should measure the diameter and compare the measurements again. The process should continue until pairs agree on the length for the diameter. This value should be recorded on the *Three-trial Data Table,* though students will need to draw an additional line in the lefthand column on their *Three-trial Data Tables* to create an extra column. Then, there will be a column for "size of circle" and one for "*D.*" This is shown in Figure 6.

Circle	*D* in <u>cm</u>	*C* in <u>cm</u>			
		Trial 1	Trial 2	Trial 3	Mean
Small	3.9	12.5	12.3	12.6	12.5
Medium	7	21.2	21.6	21.6	21.5
Large	12.3	39.5	38	41	39.5

Figure 6: *Sample data table*

Then, student pairs should measure the circumference of each circle three times to the nearest tenth of a centimeter and record each of their measurements in the data table *(Question 3B)*.

Question 4 asks students to find the mean value of their circumference measurements and to record it in their data tables. Before finding the mean value, students should examine the three values of the circumference. If the three values are very different (not within 10%), they should measure again more carefully. *Question 5* asks students why they should find the mean value of the circumference measurements. Since the process of measuring the circumference involves more steps than measuring the diameter, it is likely to have more experimental error. Finding the mean value helps to eliminate some of the experimental error. A sample data table is shown in Figure 6.

Part 3. Graphing the Data

Question 6 asks students to plot a graph for their data on *Centimeter Graph Paper*. Students should determine whether a bar or a point graph is appropriate for the data. In this experiment both variables—

circumference and diameter—are numerical. Since both variables are numerical and we are going to use patterns on the graph to make predictions, a point graph is the best choice.

Students will need to scale their graphs to at least 100 centimeters on the vertical axis and 25 centimeters on the horizontal axis to answer *Question 9.* Students should plot the diameter on the horizontal axis and the circumference on the vertical axis. A sample graph is shown in Figure 7.

Part 4. Analyzing the Results

The points on students' graphs should suggest a line *(Question 7).* Students should draw a best-fit line for their data points as shown in Figure 7.

Questions 8–9 require students to interpolate or extrapolate information using the best-fit line. Students should show their work on their graphs. A diameter of 5 centimeters has a circumference of approximately 15 centimeters while a circumference of 70 centimeters has a diameter of approximately 22 centimeters as shown on the sample graph. Sample work has been drawn on the graph in Figure 7.

Question 10 begins the exploration into the exact relationship between circumference and diameter. Students are asked to use points on their line to find three approximately equal ratios. Using points on their line, they record the values of the circumference and diameter of three circles, write the circumference over the diameter as a fraction, then divide the circumference by the diameters (see Figure 8). Encourage students to try to find points on the grid lines, since this will result in more accurate values. Students should notice that their answers for the three ratios in *Question 10* result in approximately the same number. For the sample graph shown in Figure 7, the ratios are approximately 3.1 to 3.2.

Diameter	Circumference	$\frac{C}{D}$	$C \div D$
4 cm	12.5 cm	$\frac{12.5}{4}$	3.1
8 cm	25 cm	$\frac{25}{8}$	3.1
22 cm	70 cm	$\frac{70}{22}$	3.2
30 cm	95 cm	$\frac{95}{30}$	3.2

Figure 8: *A completed table for Question 10 using the graph in Figure 7*

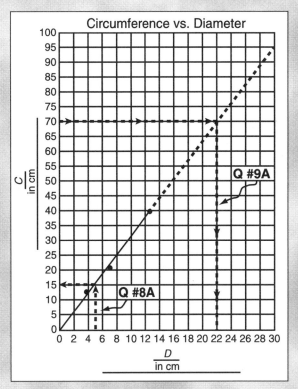

Figure 7: *Sample graph*

Graph

6. Make a graph of your data.
   - Decide whether to make a bar graph or a point graph.
   - Plot the diameter on the horizontal axis and the circumference on the vertical axis.
   - Scale your graph to at least 100 centimeters for the circumference and 25 centimeters for the diameter.

Discuss

Use your graph to answer the following questions. Show your work on your graph.

7. A. Describe your graph.
   B. If the points on your graph suggest a line, use a ruler to draw a best-fit line.

8. A. If a circle has a diameter of 5 centimeters, what is its circumference?
   B. Did you use interpolation or extrapolation?

9. A. If a circle has a circumference of 70 centimeters, what is its diameter?
   B. Did you use interpolation or extrapolation?

10. Use points on your line to find three ratios. Complete a table like the one shown here. The first row in the table shows an example. (Do not include this example in your data table.)

Diameter	Circumference	$\frac{C}{D}$	$C \div D$
4 cm	12.5 cm	$\frac{12.5}{4}$	3.1

11. Is the ratio about the same for each diameter?

Circumference vs. Diameter

Student Guide - Page 430

The ratio of the circumference to the diameter of a circle is a special number in mathematics. It is called **pi** (pronounced "pie"). The symbol for pi is the Greek letter π.

> **Historical Note**
>
> π is a nonrepeating decimal that goes on and on forever. One of the earliest good estimates for π was made by a famous Greek mathematician named Archimedes in about 240 BCE. Archimedes' estimate for π was correct to two decimal places (3.14). Today, mathematicians, with the help of computers, have accurately calculated π to billions of decimal places.

12. Press the π key on your calculator. Compare the number in the window of your calculator to the numbers in the last column of the data table in Question 10. They should be close.

13. A. Copy the table at the right and find the missing values. Use the π key on your calculator and round your answers to the nearest hundredth.

Diameter	Circumference	$\frac{C}{D}$	C ÷ D
8 cm	25.13 cm		
10 cm			3.14
26 cm			3.14
	12 cm		3.14
	6 cm		3.14

   B. Write a number sentence using C and D that tells how to find the diameter of a circle if the circumference is known. Remember, this kind of number sentence is called a **formula**.

   C. Write a formula using C and D that tells how to find the circumference of a circle if the diameter is known.

14. The diameter of a circle is 20 cm.

   A. Estimate the circumference using "3" for π.

   B. Use paper and pencil and "3.14" for π to get a better estimate of the circumference.

   C. Use your calculator and the π key. Compare your answers.

15. A. Use your formula to find the circumference of a circle with a diameter of 24.5 cm. Give your answer to the nearest tenth of a centimeter.

   B. Use your formula to find the diameter of a circle with a circumference of 48 cm. Give your answer to the nearest tenth of a centimeter.

Circumference vs. Diameter   SG · Grade 5 · Unit 14 · Lesson 2 431

Student Guide - Page 431

There is a definite relationship between the circumference and the diameter of a circle.

- The circumference of a circle is equal to the diameter of the same circle times π. This means that C = π × D.
- The diameter of a circle is equal to the circumference of the same circle divided by π. This means that D = C ÷ π.

Use the formulas for finding the circumference or the diameter of a circle to solve the following problems. Use the π key on your calculator.

16. Nila measured the circumference of a circle as $9\frac{1}{4}$ inches. Find the diameter. Round your answer to the nearest inch.

17. Brandon measured the diameter of a circle as 87 cm. Find the circumference. Round your answer to the nearest tenth of a centimeter.

18. Copy the table at the right. Then, find the missing values of D (diameter) and C (circumference). Round answers to the nearest tenth of a centimeter.

D	C
15 cm	
30 cm	
	14 cm
	60 cm

In Questions 19–21, round all answers to the nearest centimeter. Estimate to see if your answers are reasonable.

19. A tire on a car has an inside diameter of 43 centimeters and an outside diameter of 71 centimeters.

   A. What is the inner circumference?

   B. What is the outer circumference?

   C. How far will the tire roll in one turn?

432 SG · Grade 5 · Unit 14 · Lesson 2   Circumference vs. Diameter

Student Guide - Page 432

Question 11A asks students whether the ratios of the circumference to the diameter are approximately equal. Although we can never measure exactly, if we could, the ratio would be exactly equal to a special number called π (pi). π is a little bit more than 3. A good estimate is 3.14. We can never exactly get the actual ratio by computing.

> **Content Note**
>
> $\frac{C}{D}$ — We do not use units when we write the ratio of circumference to diameter, since the ratio is the same no matter what units we use. That is, $\frac{C}{D}$ is always equal to π, a pure number with no units.

A discussion about π follows *Question 11.* Make sure all students can find π on their calculator. On some calculators, the [SHIFT] or [2nd] key must be pressed before pressing π *(Question 12).*

In *Question 13A* students are asked to find missing values in a table relating circumference and diameter. Lead students to realize that by multiplying the diameter by π, we can find the circumference (C = πD). To find the diameter, given the circumference, we divide circumference by π (D = C ÷ π). For better accuracy, have students use the π key on the calculator. Students then use this relationship to solve problems.

Question 14 leads students to think more about accuracy. Since the π key on the calculator gives the best estimate for π, the most accurate answer is obtained by using the π key.

Following *Question 15,* the relationship between circumference and diameter is spelled out formally in words and symbolically in formulas to assist students when working through a variety of problems. You may need to give students additional problems where they know either the circumference or the diameter and have to find the other to give them practice working with the formulas. For example, if the diameter is 7 cm, find the circumference. If the circumference is 20 cm, find the diameter.

Questions 16–22 ask students to apply the relationship for circumference and diameter to problems without data tables or graphs as aids. Encourage students to use the π key on their calculators.

Question 19 associates circumference and diameter with a practical application. You may need to remind students that the tire travels a distance equal to the circumference of the circle in one turn. Knowing this will help students solve *Questions 20 and 22* and homework *Question 7.*

20. One wheel on Frank's chair has a diameter of 64 centimeters. If he goes to the store and back, a distance of 3000 meters, how many turns does the wheel make?

21. It takes 30 fifth graders, arms outstretched, to surround a Giant Sequoia tree. Estimate the tree's diameter. (*Hint:* An average fifth grader's arm span is about 140 cm.)

22. A bicycle wheel rolls 75 inches with one turn of the wheel. What is the diameter of the wheel to the nearest inch?

Homework

1. Use your calculator to find the circumference of a circle that has a diameter of 3367 inches. Round your answer to the nearest inch.
2. Use your calculator to find the diameter of a circle that has a circumference of 82,771 inches. Round your answer to the nearest inch.

Professor Peabody was having fun exploring different numbers for the circumference and the diameter of circles on his calculator.

Circumference vs. Diameter SG · Grade 5 · Unit 14 · Lesson 2 433

***Student Guide* - Page 433**

Suggestions for Teaching the Lesson

Math Facts

DPP items E and G practice the division facts.

Homework and Practice

- Assign the Homework section in the *Student Guide.*
- Use DPP items C, D, F, and H. Bit C practices mental math with decimals. Task D is a game that develops number sense. Task F provides practice using the relationship between circumference and diameter. Task H explores divisibility by 2 and 4.
- Assign Parts 2 and 3 of the Home Practice. Part 2 reviews order of operations. Part 3 explores the relationship between circumference and diameter.

Answers for Parts 2 and 3 of the Home Practice can be found in the Answer Key at the end of this lesson and at the end of this unit.

Daily Practice and Problems: Tasks for Lesson 2

D. Task: Fractions *Digits Game* (URG p. 11)

Draw boxes like these on your paper.

$$\frac{\square}{\square} + \frac{\square}{\square} < 1$$

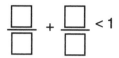

As your teacher or classmate chooses 4 digits from a deck of 6 digit cards, place them in the boxes. Try to make the sum of the two fractions as close to one as possible, but not equal to or greater than one. Remember that each digit can be chosen only once. Once you place a digit, it cannot be moved.

F. Task: Spilled Ink (URG p. 12)

Professor Peabody spilled some ink on his *Circumference vs. Diameter* data table. Solve for the numbers that are covered in ink.

D Circle	in cm	*C* in cm Trial 1	Trial 2	Trial 3	Mean
small	3	9.5		9.7	9.6
medium	9.2	28.8	28.8	28.9	
large	12.6		39.6	39.5	39.6

H. Task: Multiples of 2 and 4 (URG p. 13)

Irma studies the multiples of 4 and notices that 48, 40, 20, 16, and 32 are all divisible by 2 as well as 4. Therefore, Irma believes all numbers that are divisible by 2 must also be divisible by 4. Is Irma correct in her thinking? Explain.

First estimate in your head. Then, use your calculator to find a better estimate of the diameter for the circles with circumferences listed in Questions 3 and 4. Round your answer to the nearest tenth of a unit.

3. $C = 942$ units

4. $C = 8075$ units

First estimate in your head. Then, use your calculator to find a better estimate of the circumference for the diameters listed in Questions 5 and 6. Round your answer to the nearest tenth of a unit.

5. $D = 9460$ units

6. $D = 5977.6$ units

7. A trundle wheel is a disk that rolls along the ground and clicks once every time it makes a complete turn. It is often used for surveying land. What is the diameter of a trundle wheel that clicks once every meter? Round your answer to the nearest hundredth of a meter.

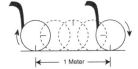

|← 1 Meter →|

Student Guide - Page 434

Suggestions for Teaching the Lesson (continued)

Assessment

*   Use the *Solving* rubric to assess students' solutions to **Question 20.** Encourage students to draw a picture to help them visualize the mathematics in this problem.

*   Assign some of the word problems in Lesson 6 *Practice and Problems* in the *Student Guide* to assess students' understanding of the relationship between circumference and diameter.

*   Use the *Going Around in Circles* Assessment Page in the *Unit Resource Guide* as a quiz.

Extension

If students have completed Lesson 4 of Unit 4, they can use 10 percent as a benchmark to check the reasonableness of their data. For example, students' data may suggest that the relationship between circumference and diameter is 3.2 or 3.1. You might want students to find the range of the class's actual data to see how accurate the class was as a whole when measuring and calculating π. You can also find the average of all the ratios $\frac{C}{D}$ and see if the average is a more accurate estimate of π.

Literature Connection

*   Lasky, Kathryn. *The Librarian Who Measured the Earth.* Little, Brown and Company, New York, 1994.

The book tells the life story of Eratosthenes, a Greek scholar who estimated the circumference of the Earth using geometry over 2000 years ago.

Software Connection

Students can use a graphing program, such as *Graph Master,* to graph and help analyze the data. If you use *Graph Master,* use diameter (D) as the independent variable and circumference (C) as the dependent variable so that diameter will go on the horizontal axis and circumference will go on the vertical axis. Students can enter the data in a table, plot the points using a scatterplot, then ask the program to draw a "line of best fit."

Resource

- Nelson, Don. "Sizing Up Trees" in *Science and Children*. Addison Wesley, Menlo Park, CA, May 1995.

Children learn ways to measure trees. They measure the circumference of a tree trunk with string and metersticks, the width of the tree's crown, and the height of the tree. You can point out the importance of the relationship $\frac{C}{D} = \pi$ since it is difficult to measure the diameter directly (without harming the tree), but it is relatively easy to measure the circumference.

Name _____ Date _____

Unit 14: Home Practice

Part 1 Division Practice
Use paper and pencil or mental math to solve the following problems. Estimate to be sure your answers are reasonable. Explain your estimation strategy for A.

A. $8965 \div 57 =$ B. $7682 \div 40 =$ C. $4128 \div 4 \div 2 =$

D. $4128 \div 8 =$ E. $7900 \div 10 =$

Part 2 Order of Operations
Solve the following problems following the order of operations. Use paper and pencil or mental math.

A. $18 \div 3 \times 7 =$ B. $15 + 24 \div 4 =$ C. $350 - 210 \div 7 =$

D. $60 + 80 \times 7 =$ E. $7^2 \times 2^2 =$ F. $30 \times 80 \div 6 =$

G. $60 \times 80 + 1200 =$ H. $4500 \div 9 - 5 =$ I. $(130 + 150) \div 4 =$

Discovery Assignment Book - Page 209

Name _____ Date _____

Part 3 Circumference vs. Diameter
Professor Peabody estimated the circumference and the diameter of some circles. He recorded his estimates below. Some of his estimates are reasonable and some of them are crazy.
If the estimate is reasonable, circle "close enough." If the estimate is not reasonable, circle "crazy."

1. Diameter = 2 cm Circumference = 6 cm Close enough Crazy
2. $D = 36$ cm $C = 12$ cm Close enough Crazy
3. $D = 15$ cm $C = 30$ cm Close enough Crazy
4. $D = 24$ cm $C = 75$ cm Close enough Crazy
5. $D = 30$ cm $C = 900$ cm Close enough Crazy
6. $D = 123$ cm $C = 1234$ cm Close enough Crazy
7. $D = 3211$ cm $C = 9633$ cm Close enough Crazy

Part 4 Function Machines
Here are two function machines. The first one takes the input number, adds 2 to it, and then multiplies the sum by 3. The second one takes the input number, multiplies it by 3, and then adds 2.
Complete both of the function machines.

Input N	Output $(N + 2) \times 3$
1	9
2	
	21
6	
9	
	30
12	
13	

Input N	Output $N \times 3 + 2$
1	5
2	
7	14
10	
	38
15	
20	

Discovery Assignment Book - Page 210

AT A GLANCE

Math Facts and Daily Practice and Problems

Assign DPP items C–H. Items C, E, and G involve facts and computation. Items D and H develop number sense. Item F explores the relationship between circumference and diameter.

Part 1. Beginning the Investigation and Drawing the Picture

1. Students choose one way to measure the circumference and the diameter of a can or lid. *(Question 1)*
2. Students draw a picture showing the variables in the experiment. *(Question 2)*

Part 2. Collecting the Data

1. Students measure the diameter and circumference of at least three circles and record their measurements in a data table. *(Question 3)*
2. Students find the mean value of the circumference for each of their circles and record it in their data tables. *(Questions 4–5)*

Part 3. Graphing the Data

Students plot the circumference on the vertical axis and the diameter on the horizontal axis. *(Question 6)*

Part 4. Analyzing the Results

1. Students fit a line through their points. *(Question 7)*
2. Students use interpolation, extrapolation, and ratios to find their measured relationship between circumference and diameter. *(Questions 8–10)*
3. Students learn that the relationship between circumference and diameter is a special number in mathematics, π. *(Question 11)*
4. Students use circumference, diameter, and π to solve problems. *(Questions 12–22)*

Homework

1. Assign the Homework section in the *Circumference vs. Diameter* Activity Pages.
2. Assign Parts 2 and 3 of the Home Practice.

Assessment

1. Use the *Solving* rubric to assess students' responses to *Question 20* in the Explore section.
2. Use some of the word problems in the *Student Guide* in Lesson 6 *Practice and Problems* as an assessment.
3. Students complete the *Going Around in Circles* Assessment Page in the *Unit Resource Guide*.

Notes:

Name _____   Date _____

Going Around in Circles

1. Estimate the diameter of a circle with a circumference of 120 centimeters. Then, use your calculator to find a better estimate. Give your answer to the nearest tenth of a centimeter.

2. Felicia did some embroidery on a hoop with a diameter of 6 inches. She wants to put lace around the outside of her work. How many whole inches of lace will she need?

3. Nicholas has a square backyard that measures 100 feet by 100 feet. Nicholas wants to put a circular swimming pool in the backyard. What is the circumference and what is the diameter of the largest swimming pool possible that will fit in the backyard? Round your answer to the nearest foot. (*Hint*: Draw a picture.)

Student Guide

Questions 1–22 (SG pp. 428–433)

1. * Use discussion of *Question 1* in the Lesson Guide.

2. *See Figure 5 in Lesson Guide 2 for a sample picture.

3–4. *Answers will vary. See Figure 6 in Lesson Guide 2 for a sample data table.

5. *Finding the mean value helps to eliminate some of the experimental error in measuring the circumference of the circles.

6. *See Figure 7 in Lesson Guide 2 for a sample graph.

7. Answers will vary.

8. **A.** *About 15 centimeters. See Figure 7 in Lesson Guide 2 which shows interpolation on the sample graph.

   B. Interpolation

9. **A.** *22 centimeters. See Figure 7 in Lesson Guide 2 which shows extrapolation on the sample graph.

   B. Extrapolation

10. *See Figure 8 in Lesson Guide 2 for a sample data table.

11. Ratios should be about the same.

12. The number in the calculator window should be close to the students' numbers in the last column of their data table in *Question 10*.

13 **A.***

Diameter	Circumference	$\frac{C}{D}$	$C \div D$
8 cm	25.13 cm	$\frac{25.13}{8}$	3.14
10 cm	31.42 cm	$\frac{31.42}{10}$	3.14
26 cm	81.68 cm	$\frac{81.68}{26}$	3.14
3.82 cm	12 cm	$\frac{12}{3.82}$	3.14
1.91 cm	6 cm	$\frac{6}{1.91}$	3.14

   B. $D = C \div \pi$

   C. $C = D \times \pi$

14. ***A.** $C = 20 \times 3 = 60$ cm

    B. $20 \times 3.14 = 62.8$ cm

    C. $20 \times \pi = 62.8$. Using 3.14 gives a much closer estimate than using 3.

15. **A.** 24.5 cm $\times \pi \approx 77.0$ cm

    B. $48 \div \pi \approx 15.3$ cm

16. $D = 3$ inches

17. $C = 273.3$ cm

18.

D	C
15 cm	47.1 cm
30 cm	94.2 cm
4.46 cm	14 cm
19.10 cm	60 cm

19. **A.** *About 135 cm

    B. About 223 cm

    C. About 223 cm

20. *About 1492 turns; $64 \times \pi \approx 201$ cm; 3000 meters = 300,000 cm; $300,000 \div 201 \approx 1492.5$

21. $140 \times 30 = 4200$ cm; $4200 \div \pi = 1337$ cm

22. 24 inches

Homework (SG pp. 433–434)

Questions 1–7

1. 10,578 inches

2. 26,347 inches

3. Since C is close to 900, and circumference is about 3 times the diameter, we can estimate the diameter to be close to 300. Using a calculator the answer is 299.8 units.

4. Since C is close to 8100, we can estimate the diameter to be close to 2700. Using a calculator the answer is 2570.4 units.

5. Since D is close to 9000, and circumference is about 3 times the diameter, we can estimate the circumference to be close to 27,000. Using a calculator the answer is 29,719.5 units.

*Answers and/or discussion are included in the Lesson Guide.

**Answers for all the Home Practice in the *Discovery Assignment Book* are at the end of the unit.

6. Since *D* is close to 6000, we can estimate the circumference to be close to 18,000. Using a calculator the answer is 18,779.2 units.

7. 31.83 cm

Discovery Assignment Book

**Home Practice (DAB pp. 209–210)

Part 2. Order of Operations

Questions A–I

  A. $6 \times 7 = 42$

  B. $15 + 6 = 21$

  C. $350 - 30 = 320$

  D. $60 + 560 = 620$

  E. $49 \times 4 = 196$

  F. $2400 \div 6 = 400$

  G. $4800 + 1200 = 6000$

  H. $500 - 5 = 495$

  I. $280 \div 4 = 70$

Part 3. Circumference vs. Diameter

Questions 1–7

  1. Close Enough

  2. Crazy

  3. Crazy

  4. Close Enough

  5. Crazy

  6. Crazy

  7. Close Enough

Unit Resource Guide

Going Around in Circles (URG p. 41)

Questions 1–3

  1. $120 \div 3 \approx 40$ cm; Using the calulator, $120 \div \pi = 38.2$ cm

  2. 19 inches

  3. The diameter of the largest swimming pool possible is 100 feet. So, the circumference is 314 feet.

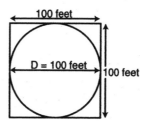

*Answers and/or discussion are included in the Lesson Guide.

**Answers for all the Home Practice in the *Discovery Assignment Book* are at the end of the unit.

Daily Practice and Problems: Bits for Lesson 3

I. Quiz: Try Some Pi (URG p. 13)

Solve the following problems using the π key on your calculator. Give your answers to the nearest tenth of a centimeter.

1. If the diameter of a circle is 4 cm, what is the circumference?

2. If the radius is 3.5 cm, what is the circumference?

3. If the circumference is 8 cm, what is the diameter?

4. If the circumference is 18 cm, what is the radius?

K. Division Fact Practice (URG p. 14)

A. $81 \div 9 = n$ B. $42 \div n = 7$

C. $n \div 3 = 9$ D. $n \div 6 = 4$

E. $15 \div n = 3$ F. $54 \div 6 = n$

M. Which Is Larger? (URG p. 15)

Which has a larger face:

A circular watch face that has a diameter of 3 cm or one that has a circumference of 9 cm? Explain how you know.

DPP Tasks and Challenge are on page 52. Suggestions for using the DPPs are on pages 52–53.

LESSON GUIDE 3

Constructing Circles with Terry

Estimated Class Sessions: 3

Students learn how to use rulers, protractors, and compasses to draw, measure, and label circles. Students construct simple figures.

Key Content

- Drawing circles using rulers, protractors, and compasses.
- Constructing simple figures with rulers, protractors, and compasses.
- Identifying the parts of a circle.

Key Vocabulary

center
central angle
chord
circumference
concentric circles
diameter
endpoint
equidistant
intersect
line segment
perpendicular
radius
vertex

Curriculum Sequence

Before This Unit

Students learned about angles and how to use a protractor in Unit 6.

Materials List

Print Materials for Students

		Math Facts and Daily Practice and Problems	Activity	Homework	Written Assessment
Student Books	**Student Guide**		*Constructing Circles with Terry* Pages 435–438	*Constructing Circles with Terry* Homework Section Pages 438–439	
	Discovery Assignment Book		*Snowman* Page 215	Home Practice Part 4 Page 210	
Teacher Resources	**Facts Resource Guide** ⊙	DPP Item 14K			
	Unit Resource Guide ⊙	DPP Items I–N Pages 13–15			DPP Item I *Quiz: Try Some Pi* Page 13 ⊙

⊙ *available on Teacher Resource CD*

All Transparency Masters, Blackline Masters, and Assessment Blackline Masters in the Unit Resource Guide are on the Teacher Resource CD.

Supplies for Each Student

compass
ruler
protractor
several sheets of blank paper
cardboard corners, optional
crayons or markers, optional

Materials for the Teacher

The Circle Transparency Master (Unit Resource Guide) Page 55
Transparency of *Snowman* Activity Page (Discovery Assignment Book) Page 215
piece of string about a meter long (to tie around a piece of chalk to use as a compass on the blackboard) or a
blackboard compass, optional

TIMS Tip

Students will have an easier time drawing a circle with a compass if several sheets of paper are stacked on top of one another to give the point of the compass a cushion to stick into. This will also keep the desk tops from being scratched. Help students learn to use the compass by instructing them to hold the compass at the top while making a circle.

It is wise to set down firm rules governing use of compasses before students begin to handle them, since the point on the compass is sharp.

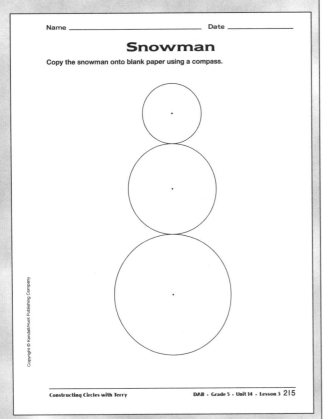

Name _____ Date _____

Snowman

Copy the snowman onto blank paper using a compass.

Constructing Circles with Terry   DAB · Grade 5 · Unit 14 · Lesson 3 215

Discovery Assignment Book - Page 215

Developing the Activity

Part 1. Drawing a Snowman

Use the *Snowman* Activity Page in the *Discovery Assignment Book* as an introduction to working with a compass. This gives students an opportunity to experiment with the compass and gain experience with it. Ask students to duplicate the snowman on a sheet of blank paper using a compass and ruler (or just a straightedge). Each student should work on his or her own snowman, but allow students to sit in groups and discuss their various strategies.

As students begin the task, make sure they understand that the original snowman's three parts touch but do not overlap and the three centers of the circles lie on a line. Their snowman must be the same. The task is more difficult than it first seems. The purpose of the activity is for students to become acquainted with some of the attributes of circles and to establish a context for discussion so that vocabulary can be introduced. Allow students to work on the activity independently without much guidance. Then, discuss together how to build the snowman.

Some of the ideas and vocabulary that should be discussed follow in the explanation of how the snowman can be drawn. You may use some of these ideas as hints if students become frustrated.

One way to duplicate the snowman:

- Draw a line through the centers of the given snowman.

- Draw a straight "working" line on your blank paper. The centers of the three new circles will be drawn on this line. The **center** of a circle is the point that is the same distance (**equidistant**) from all points on the circle. The centers of the three circles that make up the snowman are marked. The centers of the students' snowmen will be determined by using their compasses.

A **radius** is a segment connecting the center of the circle to any point on the circle. Note to students that the plural of radius is radii.

- First mark a point on the working line that will be the center of the first circle. Use the compass to measure the radius of the first circle (top circle or bottom circle) of the snowman. Students can open their compasses to this length by placing the point of the compass on the center point of the circle and the tip of the lead on the circle. Tell students that the length to which they have opened their compasses is equal to the length of the radius of the circle. They can then transfer this length to their papers and draw their first circle.

- To make the second circle, open the compass the length of the second radius. On their working line, students should place the pencil point where the working line meets **(intersects)** the first circle that is already drawn. Place the pointed part of the compass on the working line, where it falls as shown in Figure 9.

- Make the third circle in the same way as the second.

Let students decorate their snowmen with crayons or markers. This will allow for some more vocabulary discussion. For example, by placing a hat on the snowman, we first draw a **chord** as in Figure 10. A chord is defined to be a line segment connecting two points on the circle.

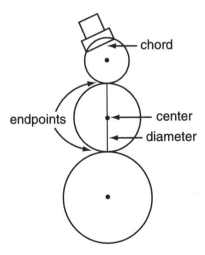

Figure 10: *Learning about circles from the snowman*

TIMS Tip

To draw circles on the blackboard, tie a string around a piece of chalk. Hold the string down at the center of the circle with one finger. Holding the string and chalk taut with the other hand, draw the circle.

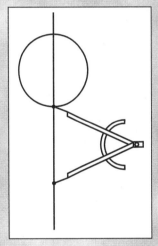

Figure 9: *Copying the snowman*

Constructing Circles with Terry

Terry is a furniture designer. Her specialty is circular tables. She makes many different tables. Terry needs to know a lot about circles to make her tables. Here are some of the terms Terry uses every day.

Central angle: An angle whose vertex is at the center of a circle.
Center: The point such that every point on a circle is the same distance from it.
Chord: Any line segment that connects two points on a circle.
Circumference: The distance around a circle.
Diameter: A segment connecting two points on a circle and going through the center of the circle. The word can also mean the length of the segment.
Radius: A line segment connecting the center of a circle to any point on the circle. The word can also mean the length of this segment.

Remember, we write $\overline{AB}$ for line segment AB. In the circle, $\overline{AB}$ is a diameter and a chord.

Constructing Circles with Terry   SG · Grade 5 · Unit 14 · Lesson 3   435

Student Guide - Page 435

Children have used the term **diameter** in the previous lessons. A diameter of a circle is a **line segment** that connects two points on the circle and goes through the center. Line segments have endpoints. The endpoints of a diameter are the points where the diameter and the circle intersect. Here, for example, the diameter of the middle circle can be the line that represents a shirtfront as shown in Figure 10.

Students may notice that half a diameter is a **radius.** This is an excellent definition of the radius. Note that the diameter is twice as long as the radius and the midpoint of the diameter is the center of the circle. Students should also see that diameters are special chords. Students may recall that the **circumference** of a circle is like the perimeter of a polygon. This is also an excellent definition. Circumference is just a special word for the perimeter of a circle.

Use *The Circle* Transparency Master on the overhead to review the terminology discussed above or draw the figure on the board. This figure is also on the first of the *Constructing Circles with Terry* Activity Pages in the *Student Guide.* Explain to students that circles are often named by their center points. Thus, the circle shown on *The Circle* Transparency Master can be called circle C. Diameters, radii, and chords are line segments and can be named by their endpoints. Remind students that line segments are named by their endpoints with a bar on top. Thus, $\overline{AB}$ is line segment AB. Ask students to name the diameter, the radii, and chords pictured on *The Circle* Transparency Master. Note the several angles formed at the center of circle C. An angle whose vertex is at the center of a circle is called a **central angle.**

Content Note

Central Angles. When a central angle is drawn in a circle, there are actually two central angles formed as shown below. Except when specifically mentioned, the angle being referred is the smaller angle, i.e., the angle whose measure is less than or equal to 180°.

Part 2. Simple Constructions

Children should have compasses, protractors, and rulers on their desks as well as several sheets of blank paper.

Discuss *Questions 1–5* together as a class. When discussing *Question 5,* explain to students that there are really two central angles DCB. Explain to the students that an angle can have degree measure greater than 180°. One of the angles DCB has measure 73°, while the other central angle has measure 360° − 73° = 287°. Discuss the other central angles pictured in circle C.

This next section will help students become familiar with terms associated with circles, related geometric vocabulary, and the use of tools with simple constructions. When asked to draw a circle of a given radius, students should place their compasses on the ruler to mark off the length as shown in Figure 11.

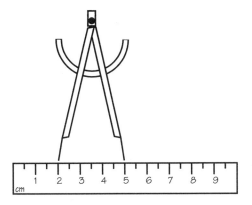

Figure 11: *Measuring 3 cm with the compass*

Ask students to draw the following:
- *Draw a circle with radius 3 cm.*
- *Draw a circle with diameter 5 inches.*
- *Draw a radius in this circle.*
- *Draw a diameter in this circle.*
- *Draw a 4-inch chord in this circle.*

Help students draw the 4-inch chord by instructing them to pick any point on the circle as one endpoint of the chord. Then, move their rulers around until they find a point on the circle 4 inches from the first point as shown in Figure 12.

Answer the questions about the circle drawn on the previous page. You will need a ruler and a protractor.

1. What is the length of the diameter of circle C?
2. What is the length of the radius of circle C?
3. What is the length of chord EF?
4. Estimate the circumference of circle C.
5. What is the measure of central angle DCB? You may need to trace the angle on a separate sheet of paper and extend a side.

Terry always makes scale drawings of the tabletops that she is going to build. Make the following drawings for Terry using a compass, ruler, and protractor.

Table 1
Table 1 is a circular table with a circular border made of a dark wood. The inside is light wood.

Directions:
A. Draw a circle with radius 6 cm.
B. Draw a circle with radius 4 cm using the same center point as the 6 cm circle.

The two circles you drew above are concentric circles. **Concentric circles** have the same center.

6. What is the distance between the two circles?

Constructing Circles with Terry

***Student Guide* - Page 436**

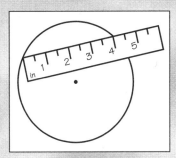

Figure 12: *Marking a 4-inch chord*

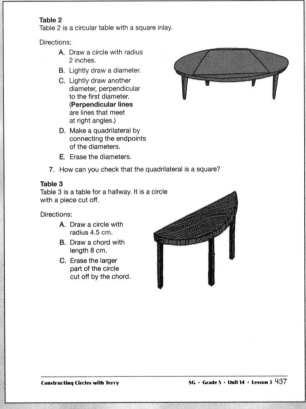

Student Guide - Page 437

Use the *Constructing Circles with Terry* Activity Pages in the *Student Guide* to discuss constructions. Terry always draws a scaled picture of the top of the table that she is building to see what the table will look like when finished. Students are asked to follow Terry's directions and help her draw the pictures. Encourage students to be neat and accurate.

You may wish to begin by asking students how they could construct the following types of tables before they open their books. Specific instructions for each of the constructions are provided in the *Student Guide*. Students can follow the instructions after they first have a chance to explore each on their own. You may wish to draw a picture of each of these types of tables on the board. See the *Student Guide* for sample pictures.

> A circular table with a circular border (Table 1 in the *Student Guide*).
>
> A circular table with a square inlay (Table 2 in the *Student Guide*).
>
> A hall table that looks like a circle with a piece cut off (Table 3 in the *Student Guide*).
>
> A wedge-shaped coffee table (Table 4 in the *Student Guide*).
>
> A countertop made from a half circle and a rectangle (Table 5 in the *Student Guide*).

After students have a chance to experiment with making the types of tables mentioned above, have them complete Tables 1 through 5 in the *Student Guide*. Discuss the constructions together as a class. Note that Table 1 asks students to draw **concentric circles,** i.e., circles that have the same center. In **Question 6,** the distance between these two circles is the difference between their radii: $6 - 4 = 2$ cm.

Students should use their protractors or cardboard corners to make the perpendicular diameters needed for Table 2. Remind students that **perpendicular** lines meet at 90° angles. Students should see that the shape formed by connecting the endpoints of the perpendicular diameters is a square. This will always be the case. Make sure your students realize that even if the square is turned on its side, as in Figure 13, the figure is still a square. For *Question 7,* children should make sure the quadrilateral is a square by checking the measures of the angles and making sure the sides are all the same length.

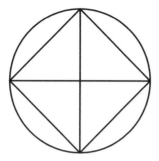

Figure 13: *Making a square by connecting perpendicular diameters*

Content Note

Squares. The reason why perpendicular diameters form a square is that squares are the only quadrilaterals whose diagonals bisect each other at right angles. To convince students that this is a square you can show that all sides and all angles are equal. Trace the figure on two sheets of transparent acetate. Rotate the top sheet 90° about the center. Do this three more times. The figures will always match proving that the sides and angles are all equal, i.e., the figure is a square.

Table 4 requires students to make a wedge-shaped coffee table. Students can first draw the circle with radius 5 cm. Then draw the two radii. Discuss with students that the radii actually make two angles, one measuring 115° and the other 360 − 115 = 245°. Recall that an angle drawn with its vertex at the center of a circle is called a central angle. After drawing the wedge, the circle can be erased.

Table 4
Table 4 is a wedge-shaped coffee table.

Directions:
  A. Lightly draw a circle of radius 5 cm.
  B. Draw two radii that make a central angle of 115°.

8. What is the measure of the other central angle? Erase the part of the circle not included in the wedge.

Table 5
Table 5 is a countertop. It looks like a rectangle with half a circle attached.

Directions:
  A. Draw a rectangle with sides $3\frac{3}{4}$ inches and $2\frac{1}{4}$ inches.
  B. Mark the midpoint of a $2\frac{1}{4}$-inch side. This is the center of the half-circle.
  C. Draw the half-circle.

Homework

Make the following scale drawings for Terry's tables and answer the questions. You will need a ruler, compass, and protractor. If the problem is impossible, say so.

1. Terry is building a circular hall table with a piece cut off.
    A. Draw a circular table with radius 2.5 cm.
    B. What is the diameter of the table?
    C. Draw a chord of length 4 cm.
    D. Erase the larger part of the table cut off by the chord.

Student Guide - Page 438

Daily Practice and Problems:
Tasks and Challenge for Lesson 3

J. Task: Function Machine (URG p. 14)

Here is a machine that takes the input number, multiplies it by 4, and subtracts 1 from the product. Thus, the rule for this machine is $N \times 4 - 1$. Complete the table for this function machine.

Input N	Output
1	3
2	
6	
7	
8	
	39
12	
13	
	71
20	

L. Task: Computation Practice
(URG p. 15)

Solve the following using paper and pencil. Estimate to be sure your answers are reasonable.

A. $28{,}468 \div 4 =$ B. $6243 - 4139 =$

C. $94 \times 24 =$ D. $3467 + 9246 =$

E. $346 \times 0.3 =$ F. $8.7 \times 0.23 =$

N. Challenge: What's My Rule?
(URG p. 15)

Find the rule for this function machine. Then, use the rule to complete the table.

Input N	Output
0	1
2	5
5	11
8	
	21
	41

Once students can follow the directions for simple constructions, encourage them to create their own. Students can create a simple construction, then challenge their peers to copy it. To encourage students to learn vocabulary in a meaningful manner, ask them to write directions as discussed in the journal prompt.

Journal Prompt
Create your own table using a compass, protractor, and ruler. Write directions for making your table. Give the directions to another student to draw the table.

Suggestions for Teaching the Lesson

Math Facts

DPP item K practices the division facts using variables.

Homework and Practice

- Homework is provided in the *Student Guide.* Students construct various figures and answer questions about the figures. They will need rulers, protractors, and compasses to complete the problems. Note that *Question 2C* is impossible, since the longest possible chord of a circle is the length of its diameter. In *Question 4,* students can either approximate the circumference in their heads ($10 \div 3 \approx 3.3$) or use their calculators to get a better approximation.

- Assign DPP items J, L, M, and N. Task J and Challenge N are function machines. Task L provides computation practice. Bit M is a problem involving circumference and diameter.

- Assign Part 4 of the Home Practice which uses function machines to review formulas.

Answers for Part 4 of the Home Practice can be found in the Answer Key at the end of this lesson and at the end of this unit.

Assessment

- Use one of the homework problems to assess students' understanding of constructing circles.

- Use DPP Bit I *Quiz: Try Some Pi* to assess students' understanding of circles.

---

2. Terry is building a different circular hall table with a piece cut off.
   A. Draw a circular table with diameter 5 cm.
   B. What is the radius of the table?
   C. Draw a chord of length 6 cm.
   D. What is the length of the longest chord possible for this circle?

3. Terry is building a triangular-shaped coffee table. Terry drew a circle with a radius of $1\frac{1}{2}$ inches. She then drew two radii so that the central angle between them measured 78°.
   A. Follow Terry's directions.
   B. What is the measure of the other central angle?
   C. Draw the chord that connects the endpoints of the radii.
   D. Erase the circle.
   E. What are the lengths of the sides of the triangle?

4. Terry drew a circle with circumference 10 cm.
   A. What is the approximate radius of this circle?
   B. Draw the circle.

5. Terry is building a table from light wood with a border made of dark wood.
   Draw two concentric circles. Make the radius of the inner circle 6 cm. Make the radius of the outer circle 3 cm more than the radius of the inner circle.

6. Terry is building a circular table with leaves that fold down to form a square.
   To see what the table will look like, she drew a circle with diameter 7 cm.
   A. Draw the circle.
   B. Draw a square inside the circle. (*Hint:* Draw 2 diameters.)
   C. Erase the diameters.
   D. What is the approximate length of a side of the square?

7. Design your own table. Make a drawing and write instructions to tell someone else how to make your table.

Constructing Circles with Terry   SG · Grade 5 · Unit 14 · Lesson 3   439

Student Guide - Page 439

Name _____ Date _____

Part 3 Circumference vs. Diameter

Professor Peabody estimated the circumference and the diameter of some circles. He recorded his estimates below. Some of his estimates are reasonable and some of them are crazy.

If the estimate is reasonable, circle "close enough." If the estimate is not reasonable, circle "crazy."

1. Diameter = 2 cm	Circumference = 6 cm	Close enough	Crazy
2. D = 36 cm	C = 12 cm	Close enough	Crazy
3. D = 15 cm	C = 30 cm	Close enough	Crazy
4. D = 24 cm	C = 75 cm	Close enough	Crazy
5. D = 30 cm	C = 900 cm	Close enough	Crazy
6. D = 123 cm	C = 1234 cm	Close enough	Crazy
7. D = 3211 cm	C = 9633 cm	Close enough	Crazy

Part 4 Function Machines

Here are two function machines. The first one takes the input number, adds 2 to it, and then multiplies the sum by 3. The second one takes the input number, multiplies it by 3, and then adds 2.
Complete both of the function machines.

Input N	Output $(N+2) \times 3$
1	9
2	
	21
6	
9	
	30
12	
13	

Input N	Output $N \times 3 + 2$
1	5
2	
	14
7	
10	
	38
15	
20	

Discovery Assignment Book - Page 210

AT A GLANCE

Math Facts and Daily Practice and Problems

Assign DPP items I–N. Items J and N are function machines. Items K and L review the division facts and paper-and-pencil computation. Bit M reviews the relationship between circumference and diameter.

Part 1. Drawing a Snowman

1. Ask students to copy the figure on the *Snowman* Activity Page in the *Discovery Assignment Book.*
2. Discuss how to duplicate the snowman.
3. Use *The Circle* Transparency Master and the *Constructing Circles with Terry* Activity Pages to discuss circles.

Part 2. Simple Constructions

1. Discuss *Questions 1–5* in the *Student Guide.*
2. Ask students to construct circles using prompts in the Lesson Guide.
3. Challenge students to devise ways of constructing different types of circular tables.
4. Students complete the *Constructing Circles with Terry* Activity Pages individually or in groups.

Homework

1. Assign the Homework section in the *Student Guide.*
2. Assign Part 4 of the Home Practice.

Assessment

1. Use DPP Bit I *Quiz: Try Some Pi.*
2. Choose one of the homework questions to use as an assessment.

Notes:

The Circle

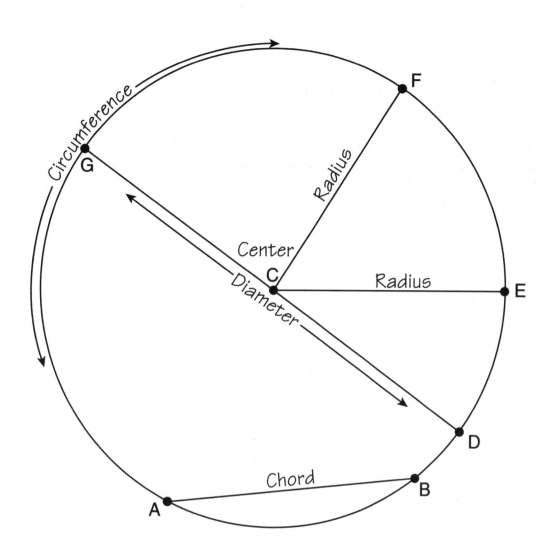

Student Guide

Questions 1–8 (SG pp. 436–438)

1. 6 cm
2. 3 cm
3. 4.9 cm
4. $C \approx 6 \times 3 = 18$ cm
5. *75°

Table 1

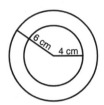

6. 2 cm

Table 2

7. * We can measure the 4 chords and the 4 angles that form the quadrilateral, and if they are all the same, then, the quadrilateral is a square.

Table 3

Table 4

8. 245°

Table 5

Homework (SG pp. 438–439)

Questions 1–7

1. **B.** 5 cm
   C.–D.

   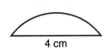

2. **B.** 2.5 cm
   C. impossible
   D. 5 cm
3. **B.** 282°
   E. About $1\frac{7}{8}$, $1\frac{1}{2}$, $1\frac{1}{2}$ inches

4. **A.** 1.59 cm

   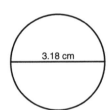

5.

   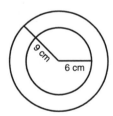

6. **D.** About 5 cm

7. Answers will vary.

---

*Answers and/or discussion are included in the Lesson Guide.

**Answers for all the Home Practice in the *Discovery Assignment Book* are at the end of the unit.

Discovery Assignment Book

**Home Practice (DAB p. 210)

Part 4. Function Machines

Input N	Output $(N + 2) \times 3$
1	9
2	12
5	21
6	24
9	33
8	30
12	42
13	45

Input N	Output $N \times 3 + 2$
1	5
2	8
4	14
7	23
10	32
12	38
15	47
20	62

Snowman (DAB p. 215)

*See Lesson Guide 3 for a discussion.

*Answers and/or discussion are included in the Lesson Guide.

**Answers for all the Home Practice in the *Discovery Assignment Book* are at the end of the unit.

Daily Practice and Problems:
Bits for Lesson 4

0. Division (URG p. 16)

A. $3200 \div 80 =$

B. $63,000 \div 70 =$

C. $210 \div 3 =$

D. $480 \div 60 =$

E. $5400 \div 900 =$

F. $2400 \div 4 =$

Q. Multiplying Fractions (URG p. 16)

Multiply using mental math whenever possible.

1. A. $\frac{1}{8} \times 16 =$ B. $\frac{3}{4} \times 12 =$

   C. $\frac{1}{10} \times 20 =$ D. $\frac{4}{5} \times 25 =$

   E. $33 \times \frac{1}{3} =$ F. $\frac{1}{8} \times \frac{8}{10} =$

2. Explain your strategy for 1D.

S. Division (URG p. 17)

Solve the following using mental math.

A. $30 \div 8 =$

B. $40 \div 9 =$

C. $45 \div 6 =$

D. $15 \div 4 =$

E. $34 \div 7 =$

F. $62 \div 8 =$

DPP Tasks are on page 64. Suggestions for using the DPPs are on pages 64–65.

Complex Constructions

Estimated Class Sessions: 3

Students use a ruler, compass, and protractor to construct geometric figures. Creating and describing constructions familiarizes students with geometric vocabulary and the attributes of different shapes.

Key Content

- Constructing geometric figures using a ruler, compass, and protractor.
- Using geometric language.
- Investigating, describing, and reasoning about the properties of circles and other shapes through constructions.

Key Vocabulary

arc
equilateral triangle
parallelogram
rhombus

Curriculum Sequence

Before This Unit

Students investigated angles and properties of polygons in Unit 6.

Materials List

Print Materials for Students

	Math Facts and Daily Practice and Problems	Activity	Homework	Written Assessment
Student Books Student Guide		*Complex Constructions* Pages 440–444	*Complex Constructions* Homework Section Page 444	
Discovery Assignment Book			Home Practice Part 5 Page 211	
Teacher Resources Facts Resource Guide ⊙	DPP Item 14*O*, 14P, and 14S			
Unit Resource Guide ⊙	DPP Items O–T Pages 16–18			*Circles and Constructions* Pages 69–70, 1 per student

⊙ *available on Teacher Resource CD*

All Transparency Masters, Blackline Masters, and Assessment Blackline Masters in the Unit Resource Guide are on the Teacher Resource CD.

Supplies for Each Student

ruler
compass
protractor
several sheets of blank paper
crayons, colored pencils, or markers, optional
cardboard corner, optional

Materials for the Teacher

Examples of Art Transparency Master (Unit Resource Guide) Page 71, optional
blackboard compass or chalk and string

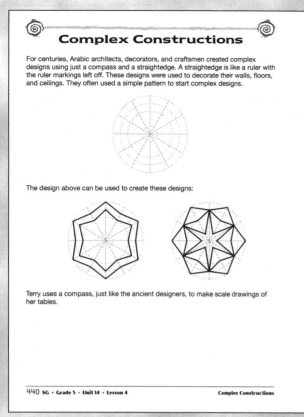

Complex Constructions

For centuries, Arabic architects, decorators, and craftsmen created complex designs using just a compass and a straightedge. A straightedge is like a ruler with the ruler markings left off. These designs were used to decorate their walls, floors, and ceilings. They often used a simple pattern to start complex designs.

The design above can be used to create these designs:

Terry uses a compass, just like the ancient designers, to make scale drawings of her tables.

Complex Constructions

Student Guide - Page 440

Developing the Activity

Students will learn more about constructing shapes using a ruler, compass, and protractor, with techniques similar to those used by ancient Arabic craftsmen and architects. Have students look at the designs at the beginning of the *Complex Constructions* Activity Pages in their *Student Guides.* Ask students how the second two designs could be made from the first design. You may wish to use the *Examples of Art* Transparency Master in the *Unit Resource Guide,* which has the three designs duplicated, to aid class discussion. Note to students that historically these constructions were made without using a ruler, i.e., with a straightedge.

Work through the following constructions, modeling the steps on the blackboard or the overhead.

Part 1. Copying a Line Segment Using a Straightedge and Compass

Draw a line segment $\overline{TU}$ and ask students how they think they could make another line segment exactly the same length, using only a compass and straightedge (without measuring with a ruler). One possible method is shown in Figure 14. The new figure is called $\overline{RS}$. In this method students use the compass to draw an arc with radius equal to the length of $\overline{TU}$. An **arc** is a connected piece of a circle, as illustrated in Figure 14. Follow the steps of the construction by starting with Step A, moving between the two columns as indicated by the steps: A, B, C, etc.

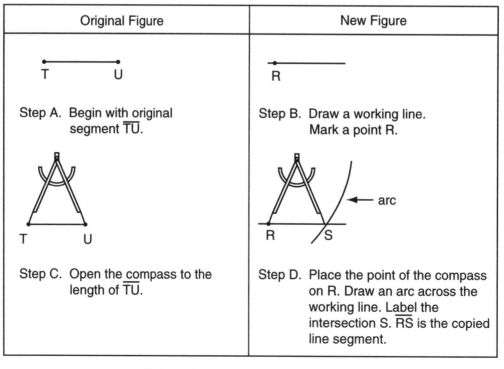

Original Figure	New Figure
Step A. Begin with original segment $\overline{TU}$.	Step B. Draw a working line. Mark a point R.
Step C. Open the compass to the length of $\overline{TU}$.	Step D. Place the point of the compass on R. Draw an arc across the working line. Label the intersection S. $\overline{RS}$ is the copied line segment.

Figure 14: *Copying a line segment*

Part 2. Constructing and Copying a Triangle

Give students a chance to think about and try to copy a triangle using only a straightedge and a compass. Incorporate their ideas in the discussion of copying a triangle.

Figure 15 shows one way to copy triangle ABC. The triangle to be constructed will be called DEF.

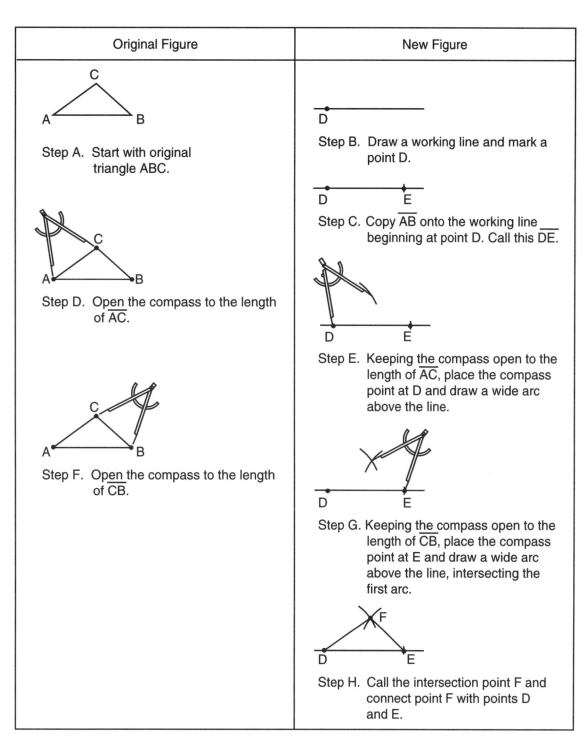

Original Figure	New Figure
Step A. Start with original triangle ABC.	Step B. Draw a working line and mark a point D.
Step D. Open the compass to the length of $\overline{AC}$.	Step C. Copy $\overline{AB}$ onto the working line beginning at point D. Call this $\overline{DE}$.
Step F. Open the compass to the length of $\overline{CB}$.	Step E. Keeping the compass open to the length of $\overline{AC}$, place the compass point at D and draw a wide arc above the line.
	Step G. Keeping the compass open to the length of $\overline{CB}$, place the compass point at E and draw a wide arc above the line, intersecting the first arc.
	Step H. Call the intersection point F and connect point F with points D and E.

Figure 15: *Copying a triangle*

Terry received an order to build a triangular coffee table. The table is to have sides with lengths of 4 feet, 6 feet, and 7 feet. Terry explained that she can use a compass to draw a picture of the table top. Terry decided to use the scale 1 cm = 1 foot.

To construct a triangle with sides 4 cm, 6 cm, and 7 cm, Terry started by measuring a length of 7 cm and naming the endpoints A and B.

Terry measured 4 cm with her compass. She drew a 4-cm arc with the center at point A as shown below. An **arc** is a part of a circle. The distance from point A to any point on the arc is 4 centimeters.

Student Guide - Page 441

Terry then measured 6 cm with her compass. She drew a 6-cm arc with the center of the circle at point B.

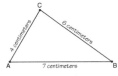

Terry drew a point at the intersection of the two arcs and named it C.

She drew $\overline{AC}$ and $\overline{BC}$. She erased the unnecessary marks. Terry now has a picture of the table top.

1. Draw a triangle DEF with sides 2.5 inches, 3 inches, and 4 inches using the same method as Terry.

2. Find the measures of the angles of the triangle you drew in Question 1.

Terry was asked to build a triangular table. Terry's scale drawing has sides 6 cm and 4 cm. The angle between these two sides is 110°.

Student Guide - Page 442

Now that students know the steps for copying a triangle, ask:

- *Make a triangle with sides of lengths 5, 6, and 7 cm. How will you begin?*

One way is described here. It is a good idea to begin by drawing a working line. Pick a point on the working line as one of the vertices. Use the compass to measure one of the lengths from a ruler and then mark off this length on the working line (or measure it off directly with a ruler). For example, the 7 cm side can be marked off as shown in Figure 16.

A   7 centimeters

Figure 16: *Constructing a triangle of sides 5, 6, and 7 cm*

Completing the construction of this triangle is similar to copying a triangle. To form the next side, measure off the next length with the compass, say 6 cm. Then, with the compass point on one of the vertices, swing an arc of this length (6 cm). Do the same with the third length (5 cm) at the other vertex. The point where the arcs intersect is the third vertex. Connect the vertices to form the triangle as shown in Figure 17.

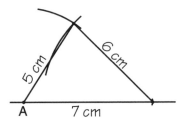

Figure 17: *Completing a triangle with sides 5, 6, and 7 cm*

Part 3. Complex Constructions

Ask students to continue reading the *Complex Constructions* Activity Pages in the *Student Guide*. Instructions for constructing a triangle with sides 4, 6, and 7 cm are discussed. Students should construct this triangle as they read the text. Then, ask students to complete *Questions 1–2.* Students should find that the measures of the angles of the triangle they constructed in *Questions 1–2* with sides 2.5, 3, and 4 inches are close to 39°, 54°, and 87°. If students have the correct angle measures, the construction will almost certainly be correct. This makes for an easy way to check student work.

Questions 3–4 ask students to construct a triangle given two sides and the angle between them. You may wish to work through this example together with the class. The length of the third side is approximately 8.3 cm.

Content Note

Side-Angle-Side. In later work in geometry, students will learn that fixing two sides and the included angle determines a unique triangle. This is known as the SAS (side-angle-side) property.

Question 5 instructs students to make a quadrilateral with opposite sides equal and all angles 90°. One way to do this is to draw the working line and measure off 2 inches. At both endpoints construct 90° angles and mark off 1-inch segments as shown in Figure 18. Connect the new endpoints (Points B and C) to complete the quadrilateral. This quadrilateral is a rectangle (and also a parallelogram).

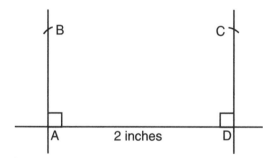

Figure 18: *Constructing a quadrilateral with opposite sides equal and 90° angles*

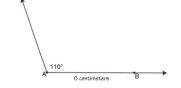

To construct the triangle, Terry drew the 6 cm length on her working line and labeled it AB. She then used her protractor to make the 110° angle using point A as the vertex.

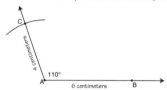

Terry marked off 4 cm on the new ray and labeled the new endpoint C.

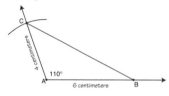

Terry knew that point C is the third vertex of her triangle. Terry connected points B and C to make her triangle.

Student Guide - Page 443

---

3. Construct the triangle Terry made on your own paper.

4. What is the length of the third side of triangle ABC?

Terry was asked to make a table that is in the shape of a quadrilateral. Terry's scale drawing has sides 1 inch, 2 inches, 1 inch, and 2 inches. The 1-inch sides are opposite each other and the angles are all 90°.

5. Construct Terry's quadrilateral.

6. What is another name for the type of quadrilateral you constructed in Question 5?

Homework

Make the following scale drawings for Terry using a compass, a protractor, and a ruler. Then, answer the questions. If the problem is impossible, say so.

1. A. A triangle with sides 3 inches, 4 inches, and 5 inches.
   B. What are the angle measures of the triangle?

2. A. A triangle with all three sides measuring 2 inches.
   B. What are the angle measures of the triangle?

3. A. A triangle with sides 15 cm, 10 cm, and 3 cm.
   B. What are the angle measures of the triangle?

4. A. A triangle with sides 10 cm and 18 cm. The angle between the two sides is 45°.
   B. What is the length of the third side?

5. A. Quadrilateral ABCD with sides 10 cm, 5 cm, 10 cm, and 5 cm. Make the 10-cm sides opposite each other. ∠A = 50° and ∠B = 130°.
   B. What are the measures of ∠C and ∠D?

6. A. Quadrilateral EFGH with sides all 10 cm and ∠E = 60°, ∠F = 120°.
   B. What type of quadrilateral is this?

7. A. Quadrilateral JKLM with sides 8 cm, 8 cm, 8 cm, and 6 cm, and ∠J = 90°.
   B. What is the sum of the angles of the quadrilateral?

8. The only instructions Terry was given for her last order was to build a triangular coffee table with angles 30, 60, and 90 degrees. Construct a drawing for Terry.

Student Guide - Page 444

Daily Practice and Problems: Tasks for Lesson 4

P. Task: Prime Factors
(URG p. 16)

Write each of the following numbers as a product of primes using exponents. Use factor trees to organize your work.

A. 3600

B. 2800

C. 4500

R. Task: Shirts (URG p. 17)

A closet has 20 shirts.

1. $\frac{1}{5}$ of the shirts are dress shirts. How many dress shirts are in the closet?

2. $\frac{1}{2}$ of the dress shirts are white.

    A. How many shirts are white dress shirts?

    B. What fraction of the shirts in the closet are white dress shirts?

3. $\frac{1}{2}$ of the shirts are work shirts. How many work shirts are in the closet?

4. The rest of the shirts are t-shirts. What fraction of the shirts are t-shirts?

T. Task: Fractions and Mixed Numbers (URG p. 18)

1. Rewrite each of the following as mixed numbers with no improper fractions. All fractions should be in lowest terms.

    A. $8\frac{10}{6}$

    B. $\frac{27}{6}$

    C. $3\frac{9}{4}$

    D. $\frac{88}{12}$

2. A. $3\frac{1}{8} + 7\frac{2}{3} =$

    B. $4\frac{5}{6} + 1\frac{5}{12} =$

    C. $8\frac{13}{16} + 2\frac{1}{2} =$

Suggestions for Teaching the Lesson

Math Facts

Assign DPP items O, P, and S which review the division facts using multiples of ten, prime factors, and mental math.

Homework and Practice

• Assign the Homework section on the *Complex Constructions* Activity Pages. *Question 8* may be left as a challenge. The homework may be time consuming. Select some of the problems now and use others later.

You may wish to review with the class, before or after completing the assignment, what they know about the sum of the angles of a triangle and a quadrilateral. In Unit 6, students learned that the sum of the angles of a triangle is always 180° and the sum of the angles of a quadrilateral is 360°. They can use these facts to complete and check their homework. In *Question 1,* the triangle is a right triangle. In *Question 2,* remind students that a triangle with all sides equal is called an **equilateral triangle.** The angles of an equilateral triangle are all 60°. *Question 3* is impossible to construct. Students will discover this by trying to construct it or recall from Unit 6 that the sum of any two sides of a triangle must be greater than the third side. The figure constructed in *Question 5* is a parallelogram. The measure of angle C is 50° and the measure of angle D is 130°. The quadrilateral in *Question 6* is a parallelogram (It is also a rhombus since all sides are equal). To construct EFGH, draw two sides with included ∠E. Then strike arcs from points F and H (both with radius 10 cm). The point where the arcs intersect is Point G, as shown in Figure 19. Another way to construct the figure is to use a protractor to construct ∠F.

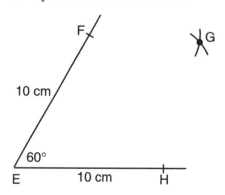

Figure 19: *Constructing a rhombus with sides 10 cm and ∠E = 60°*

Question 8 is an open-ended question. While there are infinitely many triangles that can be constructed, all the triangles will be similar. You may wish to trace some students' answers on the overhead projector and let students discover the likenesses.

- Assign DPP items Q, R, and T which review fractions.
- Assign Part 5 of the Home Practice which practices computation.

Answers for Part 5 of the Home Practice can be found in the Answer Key at the end of this lesson and at the end of this unit.

Assessment

Use the *Circles and Constructions* Assessment Pages to check students' knowledge of circles and their ability to complete simple constructions.

Extensions

Extension 1. Making Designs

Encourage students to create designs for their peers to copy. Students can discuss the different methods they use to copy the designs. Then, they can create a sample set of directions for each of the designs. You might want to have students color their designs. Coloring a design sometimes makes the relationship between the pieces involved more apparent. Creating accurate directions with appropriate vocabulary for a design is very difficult. Students may need to test their sample directions on their peers before finalizing them.

Display students' designs on a bulletin board. Students can practice copying and writing directions for a variety of designs.

Name ______________________ Date ____________

Part 5 Practicing the Operations

Use paper and pencil or mental math to solve the following. Write your answers to the division problems as mixed numbers.

A. $57 \times 3.9 =$

B. $4312 \div 6 =$

C. $\frac{3}{4} + \frac{5}{6} =$

D. $39 \times 4 =$

E. $\frac{11}{12} - \frac{3}{8} =$

F. $68 \times \frac{1}{4} =$

G. $376.2 + 78.36 =$

H. $1205.4 - 83.27 =$

I. $1835 \div 46 =$

J. $\frac{1}{8} \times \frac{2}{3} =$

K. $\frac{1}{2} \times \frac{8}{15} =$

L. $3\frac{4}{5} + 1\frac{1}{3} =$

***Discovery Assignment Book* - Page 211**

Extension 2. Constructing Perpendicular Lines and Copying Angles

• Constructing Perpendicular Lines

Figure 20 gives directions.

This construction forms 90° angles because if the two line segments, SQ and SR, are drawn, congruent triangles are formed. Since the two angles at P are con-

gruent and together make 180°, each must be 90°.

• Constructing and Copying an Angle
Figure 21 gives directions to copy ∠ABC. The angle to be constructed is ∠DEF.

To practice constructing perpendiculars, ask students to construct some shapes using a compass and ruler.

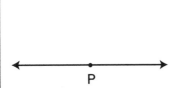

Step A. Draw a working line and label a point on the line P.

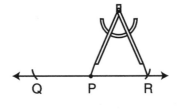

Step B. Place the point of the compass on point P and draw two arcs the same distance from P that intersect the line.

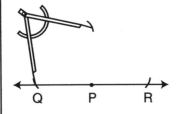

Step C. Open the compass wider and place the point of the compass at the intersection of the arc and the line. Draw an arc above the line.

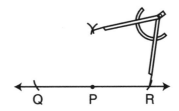

Step D. Place the point of the compass on the other intersection, keeping the compass open the same amount. Draw an arc above the line.

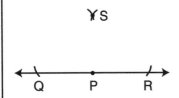

Step E. Mark a point at the intersection of the arcs above the line.

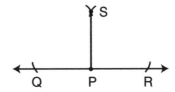

Step F. Draw a line connecting the point above the line and point P. The lines are perpendicular.

Figure 20: *Constructing perpendicular lines*

For example,

- *Construct a square with sides 10 cm.*
- *Construct a rectangle with sides 1 inch and 2 inches.*

To practice copying angles, have a student draw an angle on a piece of paper. He or she should give the paper to another student, who then copies the angle using a compass and ruler (straightedge). To check whether the angle was correctly copied, hold both pieces of paper on top of each other up to the light and see if the angles fit on top of one another.

Have students try to make designs similar to the Arabic patterns at the beginning of the lesson.

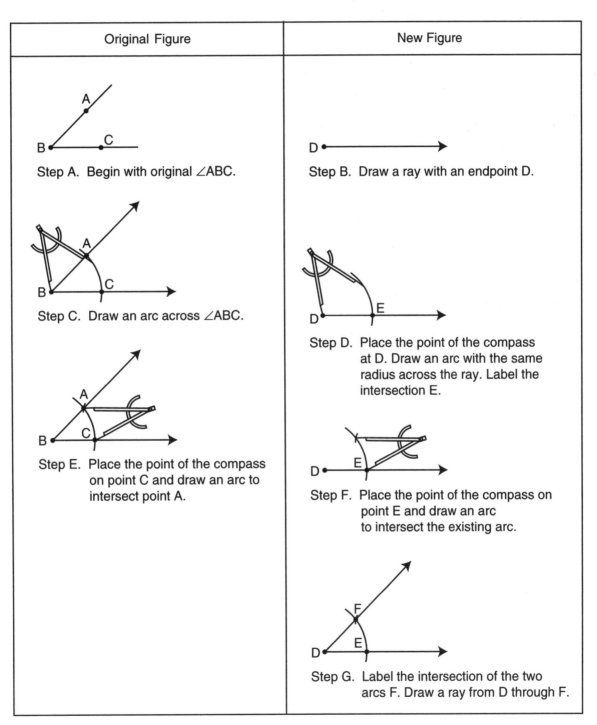

Original Figure	New Figure
Step A. Begin with original ∠ABC.	Step B. Draw a ray with an endpoint D.
Step C. Draw an arc across ∠ABC.	Step D. Place the point of the compass at D. Draw an arc with the same radius across the ray. Label the intersection E.
Step E. Place the point of the compass on point C and draw an arc to intersect point A.	Step F. Place the point of the compass on point E and draw an arc to intersect the existing arc.
	Step G. Label the intersection of the two arcs F. Draw a ray from D through F.

Figure 21: *Copying an angle*

AT A GLANCE

Math Facts and Daily Practice and Problems

Assign DPP items O–T. Bits O and S use division facts to practice mental math. Task P uses math facts to review prime factorization. Items Q, R, and T review fractions.

Developing the Activity

Discuss the designs on the first page of the *Complex Constructions* Activity Pages in the *Student Guide.*

Part 1. Copying a Line Segment Using a Straightedge and Compass

Demonstrate copying a line segment.

Part 2. Constructing and Copying a Triangle

1. Demonstrate copying a triangle.
2. Have students construct a triangle with sides 5, 6, and 7 cm.

Part 3. Complex Constructions

1. Have students read the *Complex Constructions* Activity Pages in the *Student Guide* and discuss together *Questions 1–2.*
2. Discuss *Questions 3–4,* constructing a triangle given the length of two sides and the measure of the included angle.
3. Discuss *Questions 5–6,* constructing a parallelogram given the length of the four sides.

Homework

1. Students complete the Homework section in the *Student Guide. Question 8* can be left as a challenge.
2. Assign Part 5 of the Home Practice.

Assessment

Use the *Circles and Constructions* Assessment Pages.

Notes:

Circles and Constructions

Name one of each of the following for circle C.

1. a chord _____
2. a diameter _____
3. a radius _____
4. a central angle _____
5. Find the length of the diameter in inches. _____
6. Use your calculator to find the circumference to the nearest

   tenth of an inch. _____

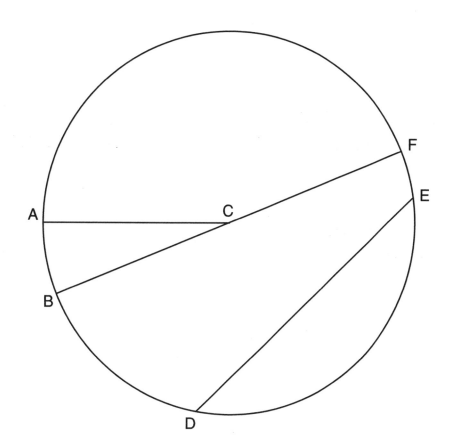

Use a compass, a ruler, and a protractor to complete the following constructions.

7. **A.** Draw a circle with a 4-cm diameter.

   B. Draw a 40-degree angle inside the circle with two radii as the sides of the angle.

   C. Find the length of the chord that connects the endpoints of the

   two radii. _____

8. **A.** Construct a triangle with two sides measuring 5 and 7 centimeters. The angle between these sides is 60°.

   B. What is the length of the third side? _____

Examples of Art

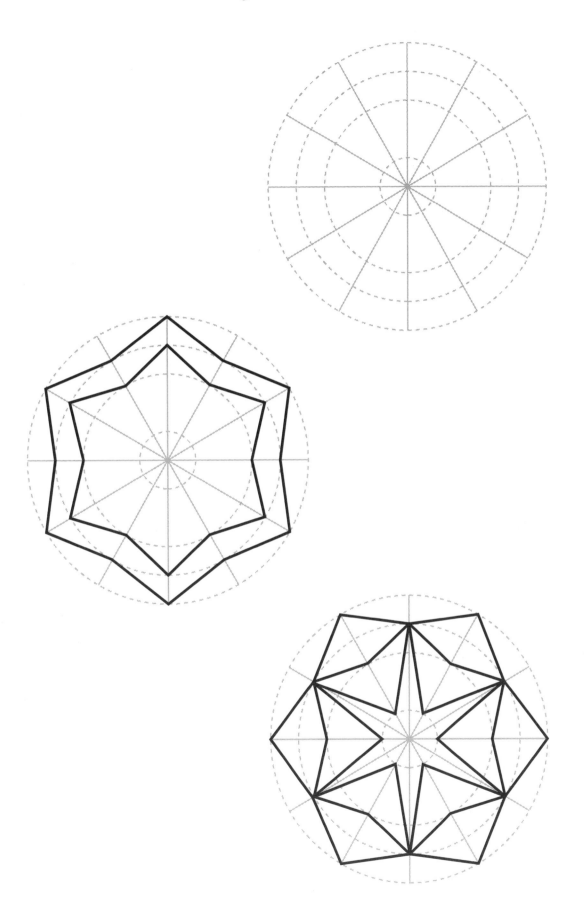

Student Guide

Questions 1–6 (SG pp. 442–444)

1–2.

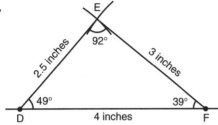

3. See the *Student Guide* for a copy of Terry's triangle.

4. 8.3 centimeters

5. *

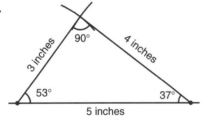

6. rectangle (and parallelogram)

Homework (SG p. 444)

Questions 1–8

1. *A.

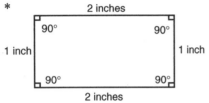

B. 53°, 37°, and 90°

2. *A.

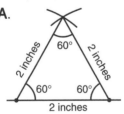

B. Each of the three angles is 60°.

3. *The problem is impossible.

4. A.

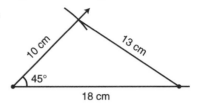

B. 13 cm

5. *A.

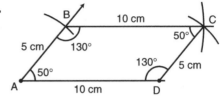

B. Angle C is 50° and angle D is 130°.

6. *A.

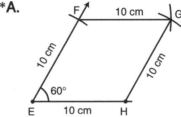

B. Parallelogram (and rhombus)

7. A. Three possible solutions are shown.

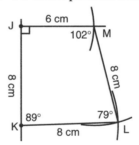 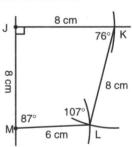

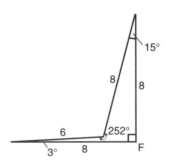

B. 360°

*Answers and/or discussion are included in the Lesson Guide.

**Answers for all the Home Practice in the *Discovery Assignment Book* are at the end of the unit.

72   URG • Grade 5 • Unit 14 • Lesson 4 • Answer Key

8. *Many possible similar triangles.

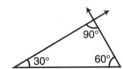

Discovery Assignment Book

**Home Practice (DAB p. 211)

Part 5. Practicing the Operations

Questions A–L

A. 222.3

B. $718\frac{2}{3}$

C. $\frac{19}{12} = 1\frac{7}{12}$

D. 156

E. $\frac{13}{24}$

F. 17

G. 454.56

H. 1122.13

I. $39\frac{41}{46}$

J. $\frac{1}{12}$

K. $\frac{4}{15}$

L. $4\frac{17}{15} = 5\frac{2}{15}$

Unit Resource Guide

Circles and Constructions (URG pp. 69–70)

Questions 1–8

1. DE or BF

2. BF

3. AC or CF or CB

4. ∠ACF or ∠BCF or ∠ACB

5. 4 inches

6. 12.6 inches

7. A–B.

8. A.

C. 1.4 cm

B. 6.2 cm

---

*Answers and/or discussion are included in the Lesson Guide.

**Answers for all the Home Practice in the *Discovery Assignment Book* are at the end of the unit.

Daily Practice and Problems: Bits for Lesson 5

V. Constructions (URG p. 18)

1. Draw a circle O with a diameter of 8 cm.

2. Draw a chord. Label it EF.

3. Draw a radius. Label it OT.

4. Draw a central angle. Label it BOV.

W. Division Fact Practice (URG p. 20)

A. $48 \div 8 =$ B. $6 \div 2 =$

C. $72 \div 9 =$ D. $32 \div 4 =$

E. $54 \div 9 =$ F. $90 \div 9 =$

G. $30 \div 3 =$ H. $45 \div 9 =$

I. $28 \div 4 =$ J. $18 \div 3 =$

K. $24 \div 3 =$ L. $9 \div 3 =$

M. $42 \div 7 =$ N. $18 \div 9 =$

O. $81 \div 9 =$ P. $12 \div 4 =$

Q. $63 \div 9 =$ R. $21 \div 3 =$

S. $15 \div 3 =$ T. $56 \div 7 =$

U. $27 \div 3 =$ V. $36 \div 9 =$

W. $24 \div 6 =$

DPP Challenges are on page 80. Suggestions for using the DPPs are on page 80.

LESSON GUIDE 5
Circle Graphs

Estimated Class Sessions: 2

Students interpret data using circle graphs. They use whole numbers, fractions, decimals, and percents to represent the data. Students then make a circle graph of the data using the small centiwheel introduced in Unit 7.

Key Content

- Making and interpreting circle graphs.
- Using fractions, decimals, and percents to represent the same quantity.
- Translating between graphs and real-world events.
- Making connections between mathematics and science.

Key Vocabulary

circle graph

Curriculum Sequence

Before This Unit

In Units 7 and 8, students changed fractions to decimals and percents. They used a centiwheel as a tool to help them translate fractions, decimals, and percents.

Materials List

Print Materials for Students

	Math Facts and Daily Practice and Problems	Activity	Homework	Written Assessment
Student Books				
Student Guide		*Circle Graphs* Pages 445–448	*Circle Graphs* Homework Section Page 449	
Discovery Assignment Book			Home Practice Part 6 Page 212 and *Make a Circle Graph* Pages 217–219	
Teacher Resources				
Facts Resource Guide	DPP Item 14W			
Unit Resource Guide	DPP Items U–X Pages 18–21			DPP Item U *Constructions* Page 18

available on Teacher Resource CD

All Transparency Masters, Blackline Masters, and Assessment Blackline Masters in the Unit Resource Guide are on the Teacher Resource CD.

Supplies for Each Student

calculator
scissors
ruler
small centiwheel
compass

Circle Graphs

 Discuss

Alexis and Frank researched endangered animals for an article they wrote for the school newspaper. They found that the United States Department of the Interior identified 607 different species of vertebrates as endangered in 1990. All vertebrates are characterized by a hard, internal skeleton including a backbone (vertebral column) and a brain enclosed in a skull. Alexis and Frank found a circle graph showing the percentage of endangered species belonging to each of these groups of vertebrates: mammals, birds, reptiles, amphibians, and fish.

Amphibians 2%
Fish 7%
Reptiles 11%
Mammals 46%
Birds 34%

Endangered Species of Vertebrates

1. What questions can Alexis and Frank answer using this graph?

2. Use the circle graph to answer the following questions:
   A. What percent of the endangered species represented in this graph are mammals?
   B. What percent of endangered species are reptiles?
   C. What percent of these species are neither reptile nor mammal?

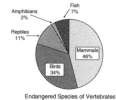

Circle Graphs   SG · Grade 5 · Unit 14 · Lesson 5 445

Student Guide - Page 445

Content Note

Endangered Species. "A species is designated as endangered when its numbers are so severely reduced that it is in danger of becoming extinct throughout all or a significant part of its range." "A species is called threatened when the population is quite small and is likely to become an endangered species in the foreseeable future."

Solomon, et al. *Biology.* 4th edition,
Saunders College Publishing, New York, 1996.

Developing the Activity

Part 1. Reading a Circle Graph

Begin this lesson by reviewing the two types of graphs students have made in the past (bar graphs and point graphs). Explain to the class that they will use a third type of graph in this lesson—a circle graph. Ask how many students have seen circle graphs before.

Read the vignette on the *Circle Graphs* Activity Pages in the *Student Guide.* In this vignette, Alexis and Frank find a circle graph displaying data about endangered species of vertebrates. The Content Note provides background information about the classes of living vertebrates. You may find this information useful if your class has not previously studied the classes of vertebrates in science.

Content Note

Vertebrates. All vertebrates are characterized by a hard internal skeleton including a backbone (vertebral column) and a brain enclosed in a skull. Living vertebrates are often divided into three classes of fishes and four classes of mostly terrestrial organisms: reptiles, amphibians, birds, and mammals. For simplicity's sake, the classes of fishes (the jawless fish, such as lamprey; cartilaginous fish, such as the shark; and the bony fish, such as the perch or the tuna) are referred to in this lesson as one group, the fish.

Mammals are defined as warm-blooded animals which give birth to live young that are nourished by the milk produced in the mammary glands. Other characteristics of mammals include being at least partially covered by hair, having an external ear, and possessing a four-chambered heart.

Fish are defined as cold-blooded aquatic animals with gills and fins.

Reptiles are cold-blooded animals that lay waterproof eggs. Identifying characteristics include the presence of lungs and a dry skin with scales or bony plates. Examples of reptiles include snakes, alligators, and turtles.

Amphibians are cold-blooded animals. They are characterized by a glandular skin without external scales. Amphibians live in the water and have gills for breathing during their early development. However, most amphibians develop lungs and limbs as adults. These adaptations allow life on land. Examples of amphibians include salamanders, frogs, and toads.

Birds are warm-blooded animals covered with feathers and possessing forelimbs modified as wings. They are well adapted for flying. However, some birds, such as penguins, ostriches, emus, and rheas, have lost the ability to fly.

In **Question 1,** students discuss what questions Alexis and Frank can answer using this graph. In this circle graph, the classes of vertebrates and the percent of species in each class are the two variables being compared. Alexis and Frank can compare the percent of species which are endangered in each class. For example, the greatest percentage of endangered vertebrate species belong to the mammal class. The classification of amphibians has the lowest percentage of endangered species among vertebrates. Discuss **Questions 2–3** in the *Student Guide*.

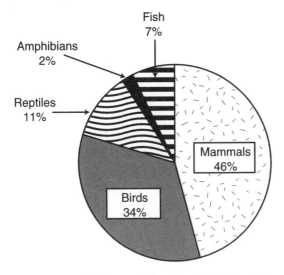

Figure 22: *Reading a circle graph*

Questions 4–6 ask students to interpret data using the circle graph. Students can work on these questions independently or with a partner. Once students have completed the questions, there should be an opportunity to check their work for accuracy before beginning their homework. Assign homework **Questions 1–6.**

Part 2. Making a Circle Graph

Begin by reading in the *Student Guide* the description of the survey that Nila and Arti made of their fifth-grade classmates. The data table they made lists the types of television shows and the number of students who prefer each type of show. In **Question 7,** students are asked how Nila and Arti must express their data in order to make a circle graph. If students do not realize that the data must be expressed as percents, have them look back at the circle graph used in Part 1 of this lesson. Ask them how the data are

---

Alexis wants to report the number of species of birds that are endangered. She used the circle graph to help her find this number. First, she looked at the graph and found that 34 percent of all endangered vertebrate species are birds. She knows that 34 percent is about $\frac{1}{3}$ of the species. Then, she looked back and saw that there are 607 total species of vertebrates that are listed as endangered. Alexis rounded 607 to 600. Finally, she found that $\frac{1}{3}$ of 600 is 200. So, she reported that about 200 species of birds are endangered.

3. A. What group of animals has about $\frac{1}{3}$ of all endangered vertebrate species?
   B. Estimate the number of species in this group that are endangered.

Use the Endangered Species circle graph to answer the following questions:

4. Estimate the number of species of reptiles that are endangered.

5. Which two groups of vertebrates together have about the same number of endangered species as reptiles?

6. A. What three groups make up about $\frac{1}{3}$ of all endangered vertebrate species?
   B. Estimate the number of species represented by these three groups.

446 SG · Grade 5 · Unit 14 · Lesson 5   **Circle Graphs**

Student Guide - Page 446

Making a Circle Graph

Nila and Arti wanted to find out what types of television shows the fifth-grade students in their school preferred. They surveyed a total of 60 students.

After organizing their data in a table, Arti suggested that they make a circle graph to display their data for the class.

Type of Show	Tally	Number of Students
Comedy	JHT JHT JHT JHT JHT JHT	30
News	JHT I	6
Drama	JHT IIII	9
Sports	JHT JHT JHT	15

7. How must Arti and Nila express their data in order to make a circle graph?

8. Copy the following data table on your paper. Use what you know about fractions, decimals, and percents to fill in the missing information.

Type of Show	Number of Students	Fraction of Students	Decimal	Percent
Comedy	30	$\frac{30}{60}$	0.5	
News	6			10%
Drama	9		0.15	
Sports	15			

After expressing their data as percents, Nila and Arti are ready to make their circle graph.

Circle Graphs   SG · Grade 5 · Unit 14 · Lesson 5 447

Student Guide - Page 447

"We can use the small centiwheels that we used in Unit 7 to help us make our circle graph," Nila said.

9. How will the small centiwheels be helpful to Nila and Arti as they make their circle graph?

10. Follow Nila's and Arti's steps to create a circle graph.
   A. Nila and Arti used a compass to draw a circle slightly larger than their centiwheel.
   B. They then began their graph by placing their small centiwheel inside the circle, making sure to match the center of the wheel with the center of their circle.

   C. Nila and Arti then used the lines of the small centiwheel to measure and mark each part of the circle graph. After they finished marking their lines, they carefully labeled their graph and added a title. Complete your circle graph of Nila and Arti's data.

Fifth Graders' Favorite Television Shows

- 10% News
- 15% Drama
- 25% Sports
- 50% Comedy

Student Guide - Page 448

represented in this graph. *Question 8* asks students to copy a data table on their paper and fill in the missing information. In this data table, students translate the number of classmates preferring each type of show to the fraction of classmates preferring each show. They then translate this fraction to a decimal, and, finally, they translate this decimal into a percent. Students have had several experiences with this type of activity during this year. If they are not sure of the procedure for translating from a fraction to a decimal, review this with them. Remind students that in order to translate the number of students preferring each type of show to a fraction, they need to know the total number of students surveyed. This number becomes the denominator of each fraction. Once they have written each fraction, they can find the decimal equivalent. Encourage students to use their calculators.

Question 10 asks students to construct the circle graph using Nila and Arti's data. Students use the small centiwheel introduced in Unit 7 to help them make a circle graph to express their data. You may need to remind students that the small centiwheel is divided into 100 equal parts. This means that the marks on the small centiwheel can be used to divide

Name _____ Date _____

Make a Circle Graph

Nicholas and Edward surveyed students in the fifth grade to find out what type of pet they would prefer to have. They surveyed 78 students and organized their results in a table.

Type of Pet	Tally	Number of Students
dogs	⫯⫯⫯ ⫯⫯⫯ ⫯⫯⫯ ⫯⫯⫯ ⫯⫯⫯ ||	27
cats	⫯⫯⫯ ⫯⫯⫯ ⫯⫯⫯ ⫯⫯⫯ ||||	24
rodents (gerbil, guinea pig, hamster, mouse, etc.)	⫯⫯⫯ ⫯⫯⫯ ||	12
reptiles or amphibians	⫯⫯⫯ |||	8
fish	|||	3
birds	||||	4

1. Nicholas and Edward want to make a circle graph to display their data. They need to express their data as percents. Complete the following chart. Use your calculator. Round each decimal to the nearest hundredth (0.01) before changing it to a percent.

Type of Pet	Number of Students	Fraction of Students	Decimal	Percent of Students
dogs	27	$\frac{27}{78}$	.3461538	35%
cats				
rodents				
reptiles or amphibians				
fish				
birds				

Discovery Assignment Book - Page 217

their circle into parts corresponding to each percent in the data table, as shown in Figure 23. This procedure is explained in the *Student Guide.* Once a graph is created, students are reminded that they need to label and title the graph.

Content Note

Circle Graphs. Circle graphs traditionally are created by finding fractions of 360°. In this lesson students find the percentage (parts per 100) of the circle used to make their circle graphs.

Once students have completed the *Circle Graphs* Activity Pages in the *Student Guide,* they are ready for the *Make a Circle Graph* Activity Pages in the *Discovery Assignment Book.* Students will need a calculator, a pair of scissors, and a ruler to complete this assignment.

📓 Journal Prompt

How is a circle graph similar to other graphs you have used? How is it different? What information can a circle graph give you?

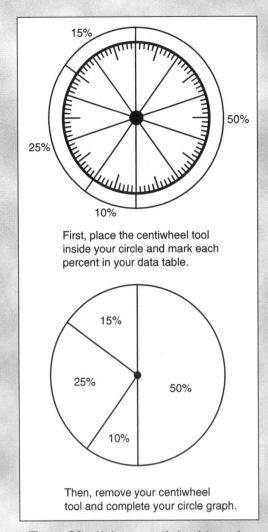

First, place the centiwheel tool inside your circle and mark each percent in your data table.

Then, remove your centiwheel tool and complete your circle graph.

Figure 23: *Using a centiwheel to make a circle graph*

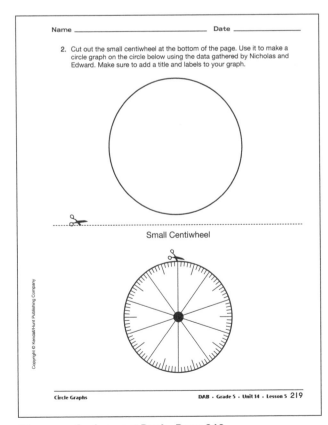

Name _____ Date _____

2. Cut out the small centiwheel at the bottom of the page. Use it to make a circle graph on the circle below using the data gathered by Nicholas and Edward. Make sure to add a title and labels to your graph.

Small Centiwheel

Circle Graphs   DAB · Grade 5 · Unit 14 · Lesson 5 219

Discovery Assignment Book - **Page 219**

Daily Practice and Problems: Challenges for Lesson 5

V. Challenge: Coordinate Geometry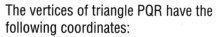
(URG p. 19)

The vertices of triangle PQR have the following coordinates:

P is at (4, 3)   Q is at (-1, -1)   R is at (3, -2)

True or false:

1. If the triangle slides 5 units to the right, the *y*-coordinate of P' will be 8.

2. If the triangle slides 4 units down, the *x*-coordinate of Q' will be -1.

3. If the triangle is flipped over the *y*-axis, the *y*-coordinates of P', Q', and R' will stay the same.

4. If the triangle slides 3 units to the left and 3 units down, the *x*- and *y*-coordinates of P', Q', and R' will all be negative.

X. Challenge: Logic at a National Park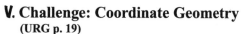
(URG p. 21)

Felicia, Brandon, and Ana visited the National Park on a field trip. Each liked best a different activity at the park (movie, fossil collection, or the nature display). Each liked a different location at the park (the quarry, the excavation, or the river bluff). Each bought a different lunch (chili, hamburger, or soup). Read these clues to see who liked what best.

A. Brandon bought a hamburger, and Ana enjoyed the movie.

B. The girl who loved fossils and the girl who liked the quarry talked to the park ranger.

C. The girl who ate chili and the girl who liked the bluff wrote notes in their books.

Suggestions for Teaching the Lesson

Math Facts

DPP item W reviews the division facts.

Homework and Practice

- After completing Part 1 of this lesson, assign *Questions 1–6* in the Homework section of the *Circle Graphs* Activity Pages in the *Student Guide*.

- After completing Part 2, assign the *Make a Circle Graph* Activity Pages in the *Discovery Assignment Book*.

- Assign Part 6 of the Home Practice which includes practice in problem solving.

Answers for Part 6 of the Home Practice can be found in the Answer Key at the end of this lesson and at the end of this unit.

Assessment

- The *Make a Circle Graph* Activity Pages can be used as an assessment.

- Use DPP item U as a quiz. Item U reviews parts of a circle.

Extensions

- DPP items V and X are challenges. Use DPP item V only with students who completed the optional lessons on flips and slides in Unit 10 Lessons 6 and 7. DPP item X is a logic puzzle.

- Ask students to design a simple survey to carry out within the classroom. Students should decide what information they wish to learn and then design a question with four or five possible responses. After surveying the students in the class, students can express their data as percentages and make circle graphs to display their data. This can be done independently or in small groups. Students can then share their graphs with the class either by presenting them or by displaying them. This activity can be expanded by including other classrooms in the survey.

Software Connection

Students can use a graphing program such as *Graph Master* to make circle graphs.

Literature Connection

Levy, Judith (ed.). *The World Almanac for Kids,* 1998. Funk and Wagnalls, Mahwah, NJ, 1997.

Resources

- Penny, Malcolm. *Endangered Animals.* The Bookwright Press, New York, 1988.

- Solomon, et al. *Biology.* 4th edition, Saunders College Publishing, New York, 1996.

- United States Department of the Interior. *Endangered and Threatened Wildlife and Plants.* 50 CRF 17.11 and 17.12. April 15, 1990.

Homework

Manny and Jessie found that people in the United States use about 338 billion gallons of water each day. They found the following circle graph showing how the water is used.

Use this circle graph to answer the following questions.

1. What percent of fresh water in the United States is used for:
   A. farming?
   B. homes?

2. Farms and factories and businesses use what percentage of fresh water in the United States?

3. A. If 338 billion gallons of fresh water are used every day, estimate the number of gallons of fresh water used each day by factories and businesses.

   B. Estimate the number of gallons of fresh water used each day for the production of electricity. Explain your strategy.

   C. Estimate the number of gallons of fresh water used each day for farming. Explain your strategy.

4. What percentage of fresh water is used for something other than the production of electricity?

5. What percentage of fresh water is not used in factories and businesses?

6. A. Which three ways that water is used make up about $\frac{1}{5}$ of the total water used each day?

   B. Estimate the number of gallons used daily by these three.

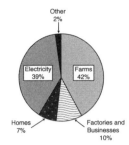

Fresh Water Use in America

Circle Graphs   SG · Grade 5 · Unit 14 · Lesson 5   449

Student Guide - Page 449

Name _____   Date _____

Part 6 Planet Power

Choose an appropriate method to solve each of the following problems. For some questions you may need to find an exact answer, while for others you may only need an estimate. For each question, you may choose to use paper and pencil, mental math, or a calculator. Use a separate sheet of paper to explain how you solved each problem.

1. Today is the premiere of the new movie *Planet Power.* Twenty-seven fifth graders were invited to see the movie. Each student received a complimentary bag of popcorn. All the bags were the same size, but some contained more popcorn than others. Brandon's bag was $\frac{3}{4}$ full. Lee Yah's bag was $\frac{1}{2}$ full. John's bag was $\frac{5}{8}$ full, and Ana's bag was $\frac{1}{4}$ full.
   A. Who had the most popcorn?

   B. Who had the least?

2. Harvey makes the popcorn for the movie theater. He bought 2 boxes of butter for the popcorn. Each box contains 4 sticks of butter. If Harvey needs to use $1\frac{3}{4}$ boxes of butter, how many sticks will he use?

3. In the movie, two space explorers are shipwrecked on a desolate planet. They decide to split up and explore the planet. Their spacecraft contains 6 canteens. Three of the canteens are full of water and three canteens are $\frac{1}{2}$ full of water. If they divide the water supply equally, how much water will each explorer get?

4. After the movie the students were invited to a party to meet one of the cast members. At the party, the students were offered cake. Of the 27 children at the party, $\frac{2}{3}$ wanted a slice of yellow cake. The rest of the students wanted a slice of chocolate cake.
   A. How many children wanted yellow cake?

   B. How many children wanted chocolate cake?

   C. If each cake is cut into 6 equal pieces, how many chocolate cakes are needed?

   D. How many yellow cakes are needed?

212 DAB · Grade 5 · Unit 14   USING CIRCLES

Discovery Assignment Book - Page 212

AT A GLANCE

Math Facts and Daily Practice and Problems

Assign DPP items U–X. Bit W reviews the division facts. For students who completed Unit 10 Lessons 6 and 7, Challenge V reviews coordinate geometry. Challenge X is a logic puzzle.

Part 1. Reading a Circle Graph

1. Review the types of graphs used in the classroom this year.
2. Introduce circle graphs by reading the vignette on the *Circle Graphs* Activity Pages in the *Student Guide* and answering *Questions 1–3*.
3. Students answer *Questions 4–6* using the Endangered Species circle graph.

Part 2. Making a Circle Graph

1. Use the Making a Circle Graph section of the *Circle Graphs* Activity Pages in the *Student Guide* to introduce this activity.
2. Review the procedure for translating a fraction to a decimal and then to a percent.
3. Discuss the procedure for using a small centiwheel to make a circle graph.

Homework

1. Assign homework *Questions 1–6* on the *Circle Graphs* Activity Pages in the *Student Guide* after students complete Part 1 of the lesson.
2. Assign the *Make a Circle Graph* Activity Pages in the *Discovery Assignment Book* after students have completed Part 2.
3. Assign Part 6 of the Home Practice.

Assessment

1. Use the *Make a Circle Graph* Activity Pages as an assessment.
2. Use DPP item U as an assessment.

Notes:

Student Guide

Questions 1–10 (SG pp. 445–448)

1. *What percent of endangered vertebrates belong to each of the 5 classes of vertebrates.

2. **A.** 46% of the endangered species of vertebrates are mammals.

   B. 11% of the endangered species of vertebrates are reptiles.

   C. 43% of the (2 + 7 + 34) of the endangered species of vertebrates are neither reptiles nor mammals.

3. **A.** mammals

   B. About 300; $\frac{1}{2}$ of 600 is 300.

4. About 60; 11% is about $\frac{1}{10}$ and $\frac{1}{10}$ of 600 is 60.

5. Fish and Amphibians

6. **A.** Fish, Amphibians, and Reptiles

   B. Fish: about 42

   Amphibians: about 12

   Reptiles: about 66

7. *The data need to be expressed as percents.

8.

Type of Show	Number of Students	Fraction of Students	Decimal	Percent
Comedy	30	$\frac{30}{60}$	0.5	50%
News	6	$\frac{6}{60}$	0.1	10%
Drama	9	$\frac{9}{60}$	0.15	15%
Sports	15	$\frac{15}{60}$	0.25	25%

9. Since the small centiwheel is divided into 100 parts, they can use it to calculate percents for the circle graphs.

10. *See the *Student Guide* for the circle graph Nila and Arti created. The circle graph is also shown in Figure 23 in Lesson Guide 5.

Homework (SG p. 449)

Questions 1–6

1. **A.** 42%

   B. 7%

2. 52%

3. Answers will vary.

   A. About 34 billion gallons

   B. About 130–140 billion gallons. 10% of 340 is about 35. 39% is close to 40% (4 × 10%) and 4 × 35 = 140.

   C. About 140 billion gallons.

4. 61%

5. 90%

6. **A.** factories and businesses, homes, and other

   B. factories and businesses: about 34 billion gallons

   homes: about 24 billion gallons

   other: about 7 billion gallons

Discovery Assignment Book

**Home Practice (DAB p. 212)

Part 6. Planet Power

Questions 1–4

1. **A.** Brandon

   B. Ana

2. 7

3. $2\frac{1}{4}$ canteens

4. **A.** 18

   B. 9

   C. 2 whole cakes

   D. 3

---

*Answers and/or discussion are included in the Lesson Guide.

**Answers for all the Home Practice in the *Discovery Assignment Book* are at the end of the unit.

Make a Circle Graph (DAB pp. 217–219)

Questions 1–2

1.

Type of Pet	Number of Students	Fraction of Students	Decimal	Percent of Students
dogs	27	$\frac{27}{78}$	.3461538	35%
cats	24	$\frac{24}{78}$	.3076923	31%
rodents	12	$\frac{12}{78}$	.1538462	15%
reptiles or amphibians	8	$\frac{8}{78}$	.1025641	10%
fish	3	$\frac{3}{78}$	.0384615	4%
birds	4	$\frac{4}{78}$	.0512821	5%

2.

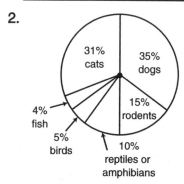

*Answers and/or discussion are included in the Lesson Guide.

**Answers for all the Home Practice in the *Discovery Assignment Book* are at the end of the unit.

LESSON GUIDE 6

Practice and Problems

Estimated
Class
Sessions:
1

Students solve a variety of multistep word problems.

Key Content

- Solving multistep word problems.
- Communicating solutions orally and in writing.
- Choosing appropriate methods and tools to calculate (calculators, paper and pencil, or mental math).

Materials List

Print Materials for Students

Student Book	Student Guide	Optional Activity
		Practice and Problems Pages 450–451

Supplies for Each Student

calculator

Practice and Problems

1. The circumference of a circle is 28 inches. Estimate the diameter.

2. The diameter of a circle is 70 centimeters. Use paper and pencil and 3.14 for π to find the circumference.

3. Use your calculator to find the circumference of a circle that has a diameter of 12,998 inches to the nearest hundredth of an inch.

4. Professor Peabody measured the diameter of a circle and recorded it as 20 inches. He then used paper and pencil to find the circumference. Professor Peabody knew he made a mistake because he knows that the diameter of a circle is always smaller than the circumference. But, the circumference he found was smaller than the diameter. Explain Professor Peabody's error.

$$\begin{array}{r} 3.14 \\ \times\ 20 \\ \hline 6280 \\ \hline 6.280 \end{array}$$

Student Guide - Page 450

5. The diameter of a large soup can is 4 inches. Its height is 5 inches.
   A. What shape did the label have before it was put on the can?
   B. What are the lengths of the sides of the label?

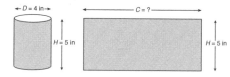

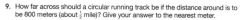

6. Lin measured the diameter of a trash can lid. It was 60.5 centimeters. Arti measured the diameter of another trash can lid. Its diameter was 5 centimeters more than Lin's trash can lid. How much longer is the circumference of Arti's trash can lid than Lin's (to the nearest tenth of a centimeter)?

7. Alexis measured the diameter of a pie tin. It was 8 inches. Manny measured the diameter of another pie tin. Its diameter was 10 inches. What is the difference in the circumferences of the two pie tins (to the nearest inch)?

8. How many people can sit at a round banquet table that is 8 feet across? (Allow 3 feet per person.)

9. How far across should a circular running track be if the distance around is to be 800 meters (about $\frac{1}{2}$ mile)? Give your answer to the nearest meter.

Student Guide - Page 451

Developing the Activity

This problem set can serve many purposes. It can present opportunities to choose appropriate methods to solve problems. Estimation, paper-and-pencil methods, and calculators are appropriate. It can also be used to supplement homework for the unit or be used as an assessment.

Suggestions for Teaching the Lesson

Homework and Practice

Assign some or all of the questions for homework.

AT A GLANCE

Developing the Activity

Students complete *Questions 1–9* on the *Practice and Problems* Activity Pages in the *Student Guide*.

Notes:

Student Guide

Questions 1–9 (SG pp. 450–451)

1. About 9 inches

2. 219.8 cm

3. 40834.42 inches

4. **A.** Since the numbers being multiplied have a total of two decimal places, the product should only have two decimal places. Professor Peabody's answer has three decimal places. With the correct number of decimal places the answer is 62.80 inches and this is bigger than the diameter.

5. **A.** rectangle
   B. C = 12.6 in, H = 5 in

6. 15.7 centimeters longer

7. 6 inches

8. 8 people

9. 267 m

*Answers and/or discussion are included in the Lesson Guide.
**Answers for all the Home Practice in the *Discovery Assignment Book* are at the end of the unit.

Discovery Assignment Book

Part 1. Division Practice

Questions A–E (DAB p. 209)

A. 157 R16. One possible strategy for estimation: $10{,}000 \div 50 = 200$

B. $192\frac{1}{20}$ or 192 R2

C. 516

D. 516

E. 790

Part 2. Order of Operations

Questions A–I (DAB p. 209)

A. $6 \times 7 = 42$

B. $15 + 6 = 21$

C. $350 - 30 = 320$

D. $60 + 560 = 620$

E. $49 \times 4 = 196$

F. $2400 \div 6 = 400$

G. $4800 + 1200 = 6000$

H. $500 - 5 = 495$

I. $280 \div 4 = 70$

Part 3. Circumference vs. Diameter

Questions 1–7 (DAB p. 210)

1. Close Enough
2. Crazy
3. Crazy
4. Close Enough
5. Crazy
6. Crazy
7. Close Enough

Part 4. Function Machines (DAB p. 210)

Input N	Output $(N + 2) \times 3$
1	9
2	12
5	21
6	24
9	33
8	30
12	42
13	45

Input N	Output $N \times 3 + 2$
1	5
2	8
4	14
7	23
10	32
12	38
15	47
20	62

Part 5. Practicing the Operations

Questions A–L (DAB p. 211)

A. 222.3

B. $718\frac{2}{3}$

C. $\frac{19}{12} = 1\frac{7}{12}$

D. 156

E. $\frac{13}{24}$

F. 17

G. 454.56

H. 1122.13

I. $39\frac{41}{46}$

J. $\frac{1}{12}$

K. $\frac{4}{15}$

L. $4\frac{17}{15} = 5\frac{2}{15}$

Part 6. Planet Power

Questions 1–4 (DAB p. 212)

1. **A.** Brandon
   B. Ana
2. 7
3. $2\frac{1}{4}$ canteens
4. **A.** 18
   B. 9
   C. 2 whole cakes
   D. 3

*Answers and/or discussion are included in the Lesson Guide.